Prospects of Career Development in Physical Education & Sports

Prospects of Career Development in Physical Education & Sports

Prof. J. S. Naruka,
Former V.C., LNIPE, Gwalior,
Director Physical Education and Sports,
University of Delhi, Delhi. 110007

Dr. R. K. S. Dagar,
Head, Deptt. of Physical Education,
Gurukula Kangri Vishwavidyalaya,
Gurukul Kangri, Hardiwar, (Uttranchal)

FRIENDS PUBLICATIONS (INDIA)
Publishers of Books on Physical Education and Sports Sciences
Delhi - 110 009

ISBN : 81-7216-066-6

Published by
Mrs. Sushil Gosain
for and on behalf of

M/s Friends Publications (India),

Showroom -
#101, 4787/23, Ansari Raod, Darya Ganj, New- Delhi - 110 002
Phones - 23246222, 23246333.

B/5-6, Mukherjee Nagar, Delhi - 110 009.
Ph. 27654826 / 27654827, # 27659446
Tel. Fax. 91-011-27654827, Mobiles. 31020441 and 9811197091
e-mail: frienpub@ndf.vsnl.net.in
frienpub@yahoo.com

Typeset by
Shri Sai Printographers
Delhi - 110 009

Printed in India
Navprabhat Printing Works.

Preface

Choosing a career is an important decision. Despite of interests in the field of Physical Education and Sports, few people have more than a superficial knowledge of the numerous career opportunities available in the field.

The book, gives you a view of various career opportunities available in the world of Sports and Physical Education. Most of the careers are inter-related and require dedication and hardwork.

An effort in writing this book has been made, keeping in mind the need of students who are really interested to join Physical Education and Sports as their career. The book contribute towards an understanding of careers opportunities and to help them while joining the realm of Physical Education and Sports.

J. S. Naruka
R. K. S. Dagar

The Authors

Prof. Jitendra Singh Naruka, is an academician of wide range of interest in Physical Education and Sports. Former Director and Vice Chancellor of Lakshmibai College of Physical Education, Gwalior, and presently working as Director, Physical Education and Sports. He is engaged in Physical Education since 1969 and has worked on various positions in institutes, like Lakshmibai National College of Physical Education (LNCPE) now known as Lakshmibai National Institute of Physical Education (LNIPE), Banaras Hindu University (BHU), Indira Gandhi Institute of Physical Education and Sports Sciences (IGIPESS), Alagappa University, University of Delhi, Jiwaji University, and Punjab University.

He was an outstanding athlete during his student life and won Best Student Gold Medal Award from LNCPE and University's First Position Gold Medal (BPE/MPE) from Jiwaji University, Gwalior.

Dr. Naruka is founder of IGIPESS, Delhi, and Director of International Olympic Committee Sponsored Sports Administrative Programme in India.

Dr. Naruka has presented various research papers at International and National level and attended various seminars and conferences in India and aborad. Dr. Naruka has travelled in the different parts of the world and is engaged with various International Organizations.

Dr. Naruka has been guiding the research scholars at Ph.D. level. He is a visiting faculty for various Universities and Organizations of Physical Education.

He has performed as member Coaching Committee (1986), Yoga Development Committee (1987), Syllabus Committee (NCERT), UGC Group of Experts in Physical Education (2001) and Chairman, Sub Committee (Phy. Edn) National Council of Teacher Education (2000), Member Sports Committee (AIU).

Delhi University had been the top among best three universities in Sports and won the coveted Maulana Abul Kalam Azad Trophy for Excellence in Sports, awarded by the Government of India (1989-1993) with Dr. Naruka as Principal Executive of Sports in the university.

Dr. R.K.S. Dagar is presently, Director and Head of the Deptt. of Physical Education, **Gurukula Kangri Vishwavidyalaya, Haridwar.** He has a vast experience of twenty-two years of service in the different fields of Physical Education and Sports. He has a long experience of organizing various inter-university championships. He has also been the observer in various inter-university championships like Weightlifting, Best Physique, Swimming, Diving, Water Polo and Boxing. He has been the member of Inter-university Sports Control Board (AIU) two times.

Dr. Dagar has attended a number of National and International Conferences, Seminars and Sports Medicine Congress and presented many papers. His research papers are accepted and published in several esteemed Journals and Magazines. He had also organized a Pre-conference Certificate on "Sports Medicine" and 13th National Conference on "Sports Psychology" in the year 2000. The proceedings of the Conference were also published by him.

Dr. Dagar is a member of several academic and professional bodies like Indian Association of Sports Medicine (IASM) and Sports Psychology Association of India (SPAI). He is also associated with various associations in the field of Games and Sports at the State and National ievels.

CONTENTS

OUR OWN PUBLICATIONS

Khel Prashikshan ke Sidhant (Principles of Sports Training) (Hindi) - Dr. A.K. Uppal.

Managing Stress. A Practical Guide - Dr. Akbar Husain / Dr. Naima K. Gulrez.

Modern Principles of Athletic Training - V.L.G. Kumar / M.M. Panda.

Netball - A Players' Guide - Jagdish Rai Sharma / Mrs. Renu Sharma.

Olympics Athens To Atlanta 1896-1996 - Dr. P.D. Sharma.

Organisation and Administration of Physical Education - Dr. S. Dheer / Radhika Kamal.

Personality Through Perception - Dr. Jagdish C. Parikh.

Physical Education and Health - Dr. A.K. Uppal / Dr. G.P. Gautam.

Physical Education and Health (combined XI and XII) PB* - Dr. A.K. Uppal / Dr. G.P. Gautam.

Physical Education and Health. XI. PB* - Dr. A.K. Uppal / Dr. G.P. Gautam.

Physical Education and Health. XII. PB* - Dr. A.K. Uppal / Dr. G.P. Gautam.

Physical Education Today and Tomorrow - Dr. S.R. Gangopadhyay.

Physical Fitness and Wellness - Dr. A.K. Uppal.

Physical Fitness How to Develop - Dr. A.K. Uppal.

Practical Guide to Physical Education, Sports and Health* - Dr. A.K. Uppal / Dr. G.P. Gautam / Shri. Vinay Malhotra / Dr. Vinod Kr. Baweja.

Prespectives in Sports Science - Dr. C.M. Muthaiah / Prof. Jitendra Mohan.

Principles of Sports Training - Dr. A.K. Uppal.

Principles of Teaching Physical Education - Dr. S.R. Sharma / Dr. Anil Kr. Vanaik.

Professional Preparation and Career Development in Physical Education and Sports Sciences - Dr. Kiran Sandhu.

Professional Preparation and Curriculum Development in Physical Education and Sports Sciences - Dr. Rakesh Gupta.

Prospects of Career Development in Physical Education and Sports - Dr. J.S. Naruka / Dr. R.K.S. Dagar.

Psychology in Sports - Prof. Gurbakhsh S. Sandhu.

Psychology of Coaching - Dr. Agyajit Singh.

Psychology of Sports - Prof. Jitendra Mohan / Prof. N.K. Chadha / Prof. S. Sultan Akhtar.

Recent Advances in Sports Psychology - Prof. Jitendra Mohan.

Research Methods for Sports Scientists - Dr. Abu Sufiyan Zilly / Prof. N.K. Chadha.

Research Methods in Physical Education, Sports and Exercise Sciences - Dr. A.M. Murthy.

Research Process and Studies in Physical Education and Exercise Sciences - Dr. Rakesh Gupta / Dr. M.S. Bedi.

Scientific Basis of Physical Education and Sports - Dr. D.K. Tandon / Dr. A.K. Uppal / Dr. P.M. Alegaonkar / Dr. Kanwaljeet Singh.

Sharir Rachna, Kriya Vigyan v Swasth Siksha (Hindi) - D.S. Dhull.

Sharirik Siksha : Tatav avm Ithas va Smast Khel Maidan avm Niyam (Hindi) - D.S. Dhull.

Sharirik Siksha Mein Paath Niyojan va Sikshan Padhatti ke Siddhanta - Ms. Seema Kaushik / Dr. Dhananjoy Shaw.

Sharirik Siksha mein Sanghathan avm Prashashan. (Hindi) - D.S. Dhull.

Sharirik Siksha avm Swasth (Hindi) (Combined XI and XII) PB* - Dr. A.K. Uppal, D.S. Dhull.

Sharirik Siksha avm Swasth (Hindi / XI) PB* - Dr. A.K. Uppal / D.S. Dhull.

Sharirik Siksha avm Swasth (Hindi / XII) PB* - Dr. A.K. Uppal / D.S. Dhull.

Sociological Foundation in Physical Education - Dr. Sita Ram Sharma.

Sports Excellence - A Psychological Pursuit - Prof. Gurbakhsh S. Sandhu / Dr. N.S. Mann.

Sports Grounds and Buildings - F.A.M. Webster.

Sports Management - S.S. Roy.

Sports Policy of India - Dr. Sita Ram Sharma / Dr. G.P. Gautam.

Sports Psychology - A Study of Indian Sportsmen - Dr. Agya Jit Singh.

Sports Quiz - Book I - Mayank Kr. Tyagi.

Sports Sociology - Dr. Kanwaljeet Singh / Inderjit Singh.

Stress Behaviour - Prof. Akbar Husain.

Teaching Children Physical Eduction - Elementary School Curriculum - Dr. Sita Ram Sharma.

Teaching Children Physical Education - Secondary School Curriculum - Dr. Sita Ram Sharma.

Teaching Children Physical Education - Senior Secondary School Curriculum - Dr. Sita Ram Sharma.

Theories in Social Work Practice - Dr. Hajira S. Kumar.

Track and Field A guide to playing and coaching - Vinay Malhotra / Abhay Singh.

Track and Field - Layout and Design - Dr. N. Govindarajulu / Dr. Rakesh Gupta.

Track and Field - Officiating Techniques - Prof. T.S. Brar.

Track and Field - Officiating Techniques (Hindi) - Prof. T.S. Brar.

Trends and Practices in Physical Education in India - Dr. Ajmer Singh / Dr. S.R. Gangopadhyay.

Volleyball - A guide to playing and coaching - Dr. P.P. Ranganathan.

Who Could Be A Better Athlete? Dr. R.K.S. Dagar.

Women Performance and Sports - Dr. Kalpana Debnath.

Women's Gymnastics - Fundamentals and Applications - Dr. Samiran Chakraborty.

Human Resource Management - Prof. N.K. Chadha.

* - Exclusive Student Edition.

Chapter - 1

Physical Education and Sports

A Dynamic Field

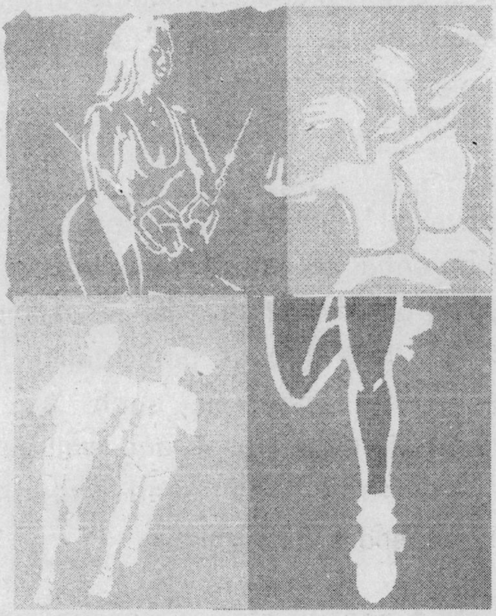

Most of people in country, in the modern era, are engaged in physical activity as they find it enjoyable. People from all age groups take part in various sport events and programmes.

This interest shows a dynamic future for the profession of Physical education and sport. Maintaining a physically active and wealthy life style is highly esteemed by many, others have not been convinced. Motivating the other group is the challenge before you to begin your physical education and sports career. The term Physical Educator is often used to encompass professionals in various careers who teaches fitness skills.

Today's physical education and sports programmes have the potential to improve the quality of life for everyone. The purpose of physcial education and sport is to enhance lives through participation in physcial activities. The objectives such as cognitive development, physical fitness and well-being, motor skill development are achieved through physical education and sports programmes.

Quality of Life - the contribution of physical education and sports

The meaning of quality of life is very wide. It covers happiness, well-being, health, fitness or permanent relief from stress, safety and absence of disease.

Quality of life in modern world means longevity. The commitment of fitness and well-being is an integral part of quality of life.

The number of factors in life have shown the importance of physical activity. The increasing rate of cardiovascular disease has contributed to a realization of the need to exercise. Poor nutritional habits and increased stress in life have adverse affect on health. Most of the people in country do not participate in any physical activity. To encourage the participation among people is the main role of physical educator.

If you are willing to accept challange to motivate people to participate in physical activities and develop program to get them involved, you can join the fascinating and ever expanding field of physical education and sport as your career beacuse future is boundless for sports and physical educators.

The contribution of physical education and sport to the quality of life can be enhanced by balancing participation in various games and sports at various level. This will give ability to learn teamwork, co-operation, communication skills, ability to lead and follow. Various sport programme can offer opportunity for fun. Development of healthy lifestyle can be achieved in society with increased fun filled physical acitivities. As a physical educator you can open its to the society

What is Physical Education and Sport?

Physical Education and Sports are inter-related activities, which overlap, and merge with each other. It includes exercise, play, games, leisure, recreation and athletics. Exercise means to practis, to condition through physical activity, Play refers to activities engaged in freely for fun, Games refers to activities to compete with significant outcomes governed by rules. Leisure and recreational activities may or may not be an outcome of physical activities athletic are definitely organized with competitive spirit in view and participation by skilled individual.

Sport today is played both for fitness and well-being . The participants in sport use their leisure time to play games for recreation. Sports are physical activities governed by formal or informal rules that involve competition with an opponent engaged for fun, recreation or reward.

Physical Education is defined as a process through which an individual obtains optimum Physical, mental and social skills and fitness throught physical activity.

Purpose of Physical Education and Sports

Physical educationist assists student to improve his Educationist life significantly. Major thrust is to improve the motor skill. Various programmes aim at increasing one's healthy life style skill. Split second decesions in 'combination with the acquired physical skill, equips oneself with the challenges in day today life spontaneously.

Objectives of Physical Education and Sport Program

The Objectives of Physical Education and sport programmes often stated more specifically than the purpose because they consist of particular learning outcomes. Physical education and sports objectives are increasingly foccussed on whole person.

The following are the objectives which can be achieved through Physical Educationand Sport programmes.

1. Physical

2. Mental

3. Psychological and Social.

1 Physical

1.Reduces risk of heart disease, diabetes, high blood pressure and other diseases.

2. Improves muscular flexibility, cardiovascular endurance.

3. Controls weight, tones body and improves body omposition.

4. Promotes over all health and fitness

5. Develops movement Skills

2. Mental

1. Improvement of academic performance
2. Increased concentration.
3. Improve of judgement,
4. Improves confidence level
5. Promotes self discipline.
6. Encourages setting goal and achievineg the goal.

3. Psychological and Social

1. Improves self esteem and Control
2. Provides an outlet for stress
3. Reduces the risk of depression
4. Promotes healthy life style.

Physical education and sport programme helps in the all around development of a person.

Physical education has verified its value as a school subject in demonstrating its definitive utility with domains of learning - cognitive, affective, and psychomotor objectives.

1. Cognitive Development
2. Affective Development
3. Physical Fitness and Motor Skills Development

Physical education and sport programme are designed to improve the quality of life and physical wellbeing . People of all ages enjoy playing games, engaging in recreational activities, and physical exercise to maintain good health. Sport provides opportunities to test skills through opponents. The all round development of the an individual is enhanced, during activity. The purpose of this is to optimize quality of life through physical activities and sport experiences. Educational objectives through cognitive development and physical fitness, motor skill development can be achieved.

Cognitive development focus on the knowledge and understanding, which includes body funtions, health, growth and development process, motor learning, game rules, skills, strategies and safety.

Effective development emphasize on social and emotional development. It includes self confidence, affiliation, judgement, character development, communication skills and fair play.

Physical fitness and motor skill development tells us about fundamentals of movement skills and physial fitness and well-being. It includes movement, concept, locomotor skill, non-locomotor movements, manupulative skills, game skills, cardiovascular endurance, muscular strength, endurance, flexibility, body composition, balance, agility, power and speed etc.

Some of the objectives are common with the allied fields of health, recreation and dance.

Careers Related to Sports, Fitness and Physical Education

Sports Science and Medicine

- Centre Director
- Sports Director
- Athletic Therapist
- Massage Therapist
- Orthopaedic Surgeon
- Paediatric Orthopaedic Surgeon
- Sports Medicine Specialist
- General Practitioner (Community Sports Medicine)
- Sports Medicine (Epidemiology / Scientist)
- Nutritionist
- Physiologist
- Biomechanics Specialist
- Biochemist
- Physiotherapist
- Growth and Development Specialist
- Sports Psychologist

- Laboratory assistant
- Kinesiologist / Physical Educator (Fitness/ Lifestyle)
- Kinesiology step/ Physical Educator (Exercise / Stress Testing)
- Personal Trainer / Fitness Instructor
- Nurse
- Computer Programmer / Systems Analyst
- Records Technician
- Receptionist

Sport and Fitness

- High performance
- National Team Director
- Coach
- Assistant Coach
- Trainer / Athletic Therapist
- High Performance Program Director
- Technical Director
- Administrative Assistant
- Recreation, Fitness and Lifestyle

- Fitness Centre Director
- Owner, Private Club
- Aerobics / Fitness Instructor
- Personal Trainer
- Diet and Nutrition Counsellor
- Recreation Administration
- Manager/Director of Facilities Operations
- Pro-Shop Manager/Director
- Manager/Director of Customer and Corporate Relations
- Merchandising Director
- Programme Director
- Outdoor Programme Director
- Manager of Racquet Courts
- Manager, Fitness and Lifestyle Centre
- Programmer/Analyst
- Budget Officer
- Marketing Co-ordinator
- Sport Administration
- Executive Director

- Programme Director
- Marketing Director
- Communications Director
- Sport Consultant
- Membership Director
- Museum Administrator

Professional Sports

- President and CEO
- Executive Vice President
- Vice President, Finance and Administration
- Vice President, Marketing and Broadcasting
- General Manager
- Director of Operations
- Scout
- Head Coach
- Assistant Coach
- Professional Athlete
- Team Trainer
- Equipment Manager
- Director, Public Relations

- Manager, Marketing and Special Events
- Director, Sales and Licensing
- Director, Advertising and Publishing
- Office Manager
- Director of Ticket Operations / Ticket Manager
- Manager, Corporate Resources
- Controller
- League Operations
- President, Players Association
- League Commissioner
- Referee/Umpire
- Game Officials
- Promotions and Advertising Manager/Director

Sport Marketing and Event Management

- Sport Marketing
- Player Agent
- Player Marketing Representative
- Endorsements Agents
- Director of Public Relations
- Players Union Negotiator

- Lawyer
- Fund Raising, Public Solicitation
- Licensing/Sponsorship Consultant
- Television Consultant, Sports
- Sports Personality
- Event management (eg, hosting the Olympic Games)
- President and CEO
- Vice President, Games
- Vice President, Finance and Controls
- Manager / Director, Sports
- Schedule and Planning Director
- Event Organizer
- Venue Design and Construction Director
- Village Design and Services Director
- Security Director
- Logistics Director
- Medical Services Director
- Manager/Director, Games Services
- Ceremonies Director

- Image Director
- Publications Director
- Promotions Director
- Manager/Director, Olympic Broadcast Organization (Host Broadcasting)
- Manager/Director, Support Services
- Human Resource Director
- Volunteer Programme Director
- Community Affairs Director

The Business of Sports

- Sports Travel/Tours Coordinator
- Owner / Manager, Sport
- Programmer (Computer / Electronic Games)

Sports Media

- Journalist
- Reporter (television, radio, print)
- Photographer
- Camera Operator
- Video Editor
- Control Room Operators

- Producer
- Director
- Play-by-Play Announcer
- Colour Commentator
- Content providers for sports-oriented websites
- see also Host Broadcasting, in Event Management

Sporting Goods

- Engineering Manager
- Director of Research and Development
- Product Designer
- Director of Marketing
- Regional Sales Representative
- Account Executive
- Commercial Equipment Representative
- Store Manager

University and College Athletics

- Athletic Director
- Budget Officer
- Sports and Information Director

- Marketing and Promotions Officer
- Sponsorship Manager
- Coaches
- Trainer/Athletic Therapist
- Strength/Conditioning Coach
- Travel Coordinator
- Campus Recreation (link to Fitness and Lifestyle)
- Physical Education (possible areas)
- Outdoor Recreation
- Business and Sport
- Dance Education
- Teacher Training
- Teacher (various disciplines)

2

Selecting a Career

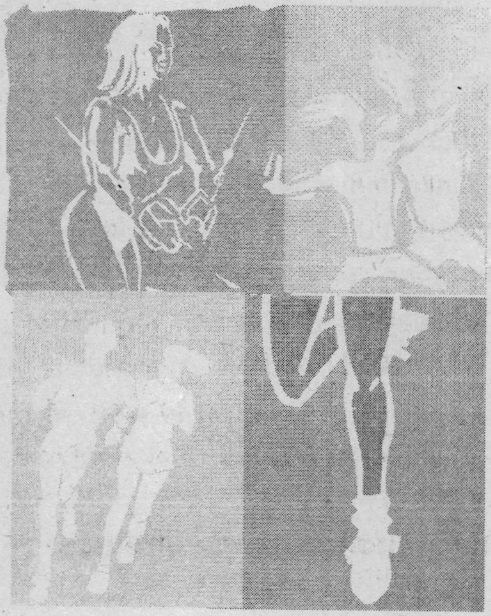

Selecting carrer in the field of Physical education and sports as per the modern concept is not so easy as more and more options are available and there are some inter related jobs too. This chapter describes the spectrum of Physical Education and sports having While selecting a career. It is essential to be prepared and to assess the objectives of your future. The assessment is not a one time job but is a ongoing process. It is not necessary that the career you choose in Physical Education and Sports has to be life time commitment.

While selecting the carrer you should identify your expectations and attitudes about it. Your attitude will decide whether you will be successfull and happy in the field. A major factor is your own concept. How you evaluate your abilities? Are you willing to listen to advices from your supervisors? Can you assess your strength and weakness? Are you motivated to do the best? Are you ready to take challenges? etc Before choosing a career, it is essential to analyse the relative importance of personal and job related factors.

Factors that influence career choices

There are many career choices availble in this field. There are some factors which play key role.

Family influence - While choosing a field, family plays a vital role. The family can be positive, negative or both, family can help in pursuing the career, may prevent their children for choosing a career in Physical education because of their lack of knowledge about the Prestigious field or on the other hand they can motivate their children to choose because of thier own practical experience. But one has to keep in mind his own attitude. while choosing a career in Physical Education Family members should be consulted but the final decision should be one's own.

The Role Model - Some people select a career because they respect and admire some one who is a role model, with whom one identifies. He may be a parent, teacher, friend or any celebroty.

Working Knowledge - The skills, knowledge abilities and experience that you acquire will influence whether you will be a success. Your confidence in accepting an initial position is based on two factors, one your ability to assimilate your basic secondly your grit and determination to excell, to reach the top.

Personal Fullfillment and Satisfaction - Job satisfaction is then utlimate decisive factor , its presence suggests possitive attitude, its absence is an indication to change.

Monetary and other benefits - It is most important as it affects the career. If a career has more monetary benefits people opt for that (are attracted towards it).

Job Security - Security too effects the career. If the career has job security and more and more choices are available for the people to choose, then more people are attracted towards it and vice versa i.e lesser job security, lesser people join it.

Job security in physical education and sport career varies. Complete fulfillment of job responsibility in some careers results in retention of position based on merit. Career in education requires earned tenure for job security.

Pros and Cones art to be weighed in the light of monetary considerations i.e. the life style one anticipates for one self, perks accompanied, the rewards you are able to visualise with in the specific period.

Career opportunities in physical education ans ports are expanding day by day. As a young professional, you should be willing to accept all the challanges and work hard to learn new ideas to gain experience.

As you decide a career, review and weigh all the above factors. Only after evaluating the most important considerations and your own personal preferences. you can objectively select a career (Physical Education).

The following are Career opportunities in Physical Education and sport-

Teaching

Elemantary schools,

Middle Schools,

Secondary. Schools,

Colleges / Universities,

Physical Education Colleges /Institutes

Fitness Development

Athletic Training

Sport Officiating

Nontraditional

Sports Club

Health Club

Sports Camp or School

Recreation-Department

Corporate or industrial fitness

Senior Citizens' Programme

Military

Dance studio

Resort

Cruise-ship

Rehabilitative

Therapeutic recreation

Cardiac Rehabilitation

Sports Medicine Clinic

Weight Control Center

Stress Management Clinic

Massage Clinic

Fitness and Nutrition Counseling

College and University

Coaching

Athletic Administration

Athletic Training

Business Management

Facility Management

Sport Management

Business and Industry

Sports Club

Health Club

Sports Camp and School

Corporate or Industrial Fitness

Theme Park and Resort

Sports Hall of Fame and Museum

Public Fitness and Recreation

Facility Management

Sport Marketing

Clothing-sales

Equipment-sales

Club Membership-Sales

Sport Communication

Sports Broadcasting

Sports Journalism

Spots Photograpy

Sports Information

Sports Marketing

Academic Counselling

Sports Officiating

Ticket Sales

Strength and Conditioning

Coach

Sports Psychology

Constant inflow of research and technique in every field change the very basic concepts during decade. One ought to assimilate keep posted with latest developments not only one's own field but also in allied fields too.

After matching your aspiratons and abilities in particular you can choose your college.

3

Planning a Career

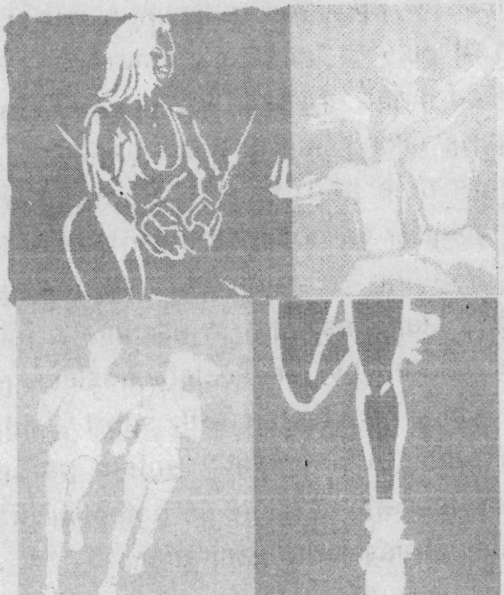

by Kiran Sandhu, IGIPESS, Vikaspuri, New-Delhi

Some of the essential elements that will be of help in making the multiple choices available in the area of sports are as follows:

(a) Motivational Dynamics

The very first factor which needs to be considered is, what motivates one to take to sport. Probably initially it is the orientation given by parents and environment, and facilities available to young ones besides the natural instinct for play, fun, enjoyment etc. From the natural form of play to game patterns and then on to more organised forms of sport, for all good reasons an individual starts taking sports more seriously, willingly spending more time and placing it on higher priority than just a hobby or an outlet. At this point of time one also starts thinking of personal development and ambitions. One starts aspiring to assume a role in life to feel more wanted by the society besides personal satisfaction. Being acquainted with sport a little more closely and being a physically active person, one naturally looks forward to sport as potential profession worthy of one's professional aspirations.

(b) Self-Assessment

Every individual is characteristically unique. In order to see as clearly as possible what kind of a person one has become during time, some kind of self-assessment is required. Such an assessment should be made in terms of the skill acquisition including academic and physical strength, liking for type of games, degree of ease/difficulty in working with other, recreational skills etc. to assess the weaknesses and the strengths of one's personality. In specific, self-assessment must lead one to realize the following traits related to sport and physical activity:

- Do programmes related to sports and physical activity spark one's interest and imagination?
- Do recreation and competitive activities attract you?
- Do you appreciate sports by participation in them or by watching them or by organizing them?
- Does watching TV or writing and recording about sport attract you ?

Such traits are tremendously important for the consideration of the development of a sports career. Self - assessment of one's interest is highly important since it is the conscious effort that enable one to expand and modify one's interest for better results.

Values, another attribute of personality, also have high relevance for planning a career in sport. The word 'value' here refers to excellence, importance, desirability

Each one of us places a high value on meeting our basic need of food, shelter, clothes and freedom etc. In addition, we must clearly visualize the salary, working conditions, service to others, job satisfaction, promotion avenues of sports career according to our personal order of preference.

(c) Course of Study

Choice of career is also dependent on the type of course of study available. In our country, at senior level, physical education is available as one of the optional subjects. But, at college and university level, the courses of study in physical education are: (1) B.P. Ed. in colleges of physical education, and (2) B.Sc(Physical Education) in general colleges.

(d) Professional Experience and Aspirations

The next and possibly more influencing factor affecting career selection in sports is the professional aspiration. In the existing set-up of sport, there are no alternative careers but for a few viable options. For decades all professional programmes have been desigened to teach and coach especially in formal and non-formal education settings. Resultantly, majority of physically active people enter sport career mainly with an aspiration to become a teacher or a coach. With this limited awareness of the possibilities of career in sports, one hardly realizes the environmental need for person with background of sport education for numerous sports related jobs. In view of this, the point of utmost concern should be to bring about a broader awareness about the sport careers like those in sports administration, fitness, rehabilitation and therapy, sales and business management, and communications.

(e) Exploring the Sport World for Career Opportunities

Developed countries provide a fairly good amount of information with regard to career opportunities through various governmental, non-governmental and professional agencies. In India. So far, not much of expert ssistance is available. But there are other possible methods one can resort to, in order to obtain best possible objective information. For example, good readers, encyclopedia and other career related material are of a good help. Talking to people having a comprehensive understanding of sport opportunities will also prove beneficial. However, once the career (s) of interest have been explored, one should:

(i) Arrange to meet a successful person in the field and ask if he or she can arrange to discuss the career field in detail;

(ii) request for information from various organisations that sponsors or serve as professional management associations within various career fields;

(iii) read professional journals, magazines, newspapers and books that may offer information on career;

(iv) acquire some knowledge through social interaction and academic deliberation at professional platforms or any other such source to get maximum information to finally cash the opportunity.

(f) Decision-Making

Consistenly poor decisions in any area of routine life from eating, drinking, money (spendings, investing), family and friends have unhappy consequences. Selecting one's career and its objective is one of the major decisions of life. Thus, obviously, a big question shall be split into a list of narrowly focused questions e.g., what career opportunities are there for those with an athletic ability, teaching aptitude, love for outdoors, administrative idea, research quest and so on. Such narrowly focused questions lead to seek more information regarding education, investment advancement etc. In short, breaking up a big question into smaller ones, requires examining all of the pros and cons and choosing for or against for reasons believed to be sound. Personal experience by virtue of part-time job, voluntary assignments etc., can help have first hand information of the work. Often, tentative choices can be made in the beginning to be later confirmed, modified or rejected.

While need to decide a career surfaces first in senior secondary school, it often recurs at the college entry. Each individual has the final and sole responsibility for his choice of career, but it need not be solitary process. One is always urged to reach out for help.

(g) Learning to Take Help

Caring people are a magnificent resource. There are people who are interested in the welfare of upcoming youngsters. Parents, counsellors, elders and adults around and techers seem to be pushing young ones to improve study and play habits in right directions, to make better use of time, and to be better prepared to take advantage of career opportunities.

The best way to test one's interest in career is to talk about it to others, especially at the critical juncture of decision making like selecting academic curriculam and competition from out of sports calendar, or while making a choice between the two job offers, or about dividing the time among studies, sports and other interests. It is advisable to speak to more than one person to weigh one's own views with theirs, remembering that it has to be one's own choice at the End.

Personal Professionalism

The first and the foremost responsibility of a profession in physical education is to present an image that reflects the purpose and goals of the discipline. One is expected to be continually participating in the dynamic pursuits of prefessional conferences, conventions and seminars as well as periodicals, journals and other ongoing research activities in sports. This brings first hand information regarding teaching coaching strategies, techniques and in-depth understanding of latest scientific disciplines underlying sports and physical education.

The right weight and a fit body are always admired in sports professionals. Beyond doubt, everybody cannot be perfect but it is within reach to present oneself as healthy and fit, a role model for society; practise what you preach.

In view of the need to invariably address small and big groups in physical education, it is highly important to be able to speak in an intelligent and effective manner. Good written expression should also be mastered to present the programme summaries, reports and future plans for effective action by the authorities and public.

It is also very essential to become active in existing sports clubs and physical education organisation. If, by chance, nothing exists in the immediate approachable environment, it would be most appropriate to organize one with the help of fellow friends and colleagues. It would become visible in professional circles for potential and qualities. It also provides an opportunity for exchange of ideas, view research and new techniques.

An effort should be initiated to build a personal library of professional materials. If expensive periodicals and journals cannot be subscribed to, a pool system may be started with the help of other members. Support of money, literature, reference and the like may go a long way in the profession.

The professionals must establish a relationship outside sports field programmes also. It is always desirable to visit, share meals, exchange views and spend leisure time with staff of other subjects. It may provide an opportunity to express oneself in the world of economics, politics, fine arts, etc. Such an effort is essentially required to strengthen and promote professional image.

Another important. trait is to offer help on your own to staff in charge for institutional programmes other than sports. The return of such an investment programmes will be in the form of much needed help during sports programmes which cannot be successfully organised individualy.

Finally, for a corporate development a sincere desire to work with others should be displayed. One must be well prepared, high spirited, flexible, open minded and willing to accept the situation as a matter of fact.

However, it is equally important to be prepared to start with, to present oneself for professional identification. Accordingly, it is essential to write a professional resume, a brief bio-data for an immediate use as and when required. A record of certificates, honours, recommendation letters, various leadership positives help and assignment record (ad-hoc and special) can be of immense help in breaking through better opportunities in the career.

As one desires to be, true professional in the area of physical education and sports, it is always expected to keep in mind that accepted traits of strong professional are being a leader and an initiator with a creative force. Community and institutional support can be ensured for conscious role model presentation, so as to achieve the objectives of physical education and sports.

In conclusion, it is submitted as a plain fact that today the only certainty has become the uncertainty of ever changing environment due to technological, political, economic and other such global factors. Hence, it is recommended to keep alert to events affecting sports world that have a significant impact on employment and career avenues. Such events are usually reported in newspapers and news-magazines. Planning a career in sport is no doubt difficult, but exciting for all the reasons. This proces can change your entire life; it contains all the adventures of unknown - the new the different and the unexplored; it is particularly one's own choice, where one charts one's own course.

Chapter 4

Physical Education

A Career in Teaching

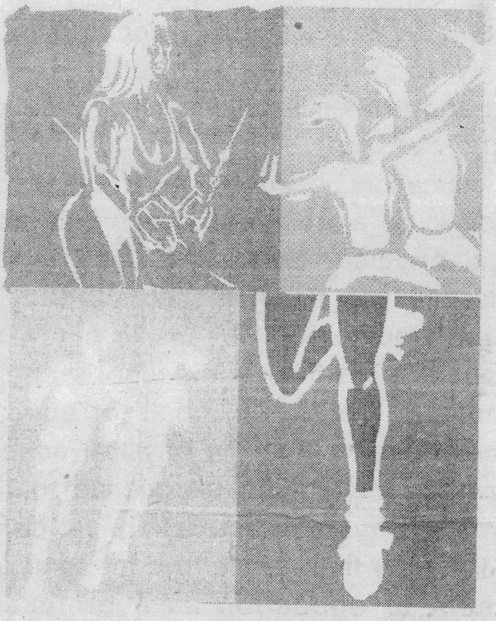

Students have always admired their physical education teachers; many have considered entering this career themselves. However, recently, because of diminshing job opportunities and the attraction of other sports careers, they have begun to look elsewhere. Some still see this as an attractive option because of the chance to work with young blood and to teach them physical education skills. Often coaches come from the ranks of physical education teachers, so this too looms as one of the attractions of the profession.

Many people in Physical Education can look back to their early experiences as students in physical education and to their involvement in athletics for their career choice. Most of students choose career in Physical education because they were good in sports and wished to be a teacher or coach they admired. But the actual physical education class that looks so inviting is only the tip of iceberg. Broad knowledge base is required through intensive study, an arry of skills through which their knowledge is applied, and a commitment to the overall goals of education. It is necessary to ensure that the physical education class is the inviting challenging experience to the student who choose Physical education as career, must possess far more than just a love for sport. A thorough commitment to education as a profession and a willingness to accept the multitude of associated responsibilities are essential.

Each student in each grade shall participate in a planned program of physical education. The planned program shall include activities which:

1. Assist each student to attain and maintain a desirable level of physical fitness.
2. Develop desirable competence for participation in sports, team spirt and games.
3. Promote an understanding between regular physical activity and health
4. Provide sports, games and other physical activities that promote self confidence and the ability to work in a group.
5. Require co-educational instruction at the elementary, middle grade and junior and high school level.

In recent years there has existed an increasing desire to educate young people to the importance of fitness, the joy of sports and athletics, and the value of lifetime sports.

Much the same as curriculum changes have occurred in other school subject

Several physical education teachers have organized such activities at their schools with success. The leisure revolution has resulted in a desire to expand participation in lifetime sports. These new directions will continue to challengeto energize the talents of physical education specialists.

Duties and Activities

Many demands and duties characterize the activities of the Physical Education teacher.

The physical education teacher engages in some of the following activities.

1. Determines the ability of students in their courses.
2. to induce suitable changes in teaching methods keeping in view the students capabilities to assimilate knowledge at a specific stage.s
3. Prepares an equipment and materials-purchase budget and maintains it once obtained.
4. Utilizes an efficient system for reporting accidents and following them up.
5. Conducts special programs for children with physiological and psychological problems.
6. Provides information to the parents and community concerning the curriculum.
7. Promotes physical fitness in the school and community.
8. Helps students to commit themselves to self-improvement.
9. Prompts non-participating learners to join class activities and stay involved.
10. Develops a wide variety of skills in students, such as: accuracy, ability, balance, co-ordination, endurance, flexibility, power, rhythm, strength, timing, and other psychomotor abilities.

The physical education instructor must maintain fitness not only as a model for students but to maintain the rigorous schedule that makes many demands upon the teacher.

Individuals who mess teaching and coaching it's truly an unbelievable commitment. This combination requires intelligence, great energy and ability, and promises great rewards.

At the class level Physical Education Teachers enjoy teaching students the athletic skills of movement, efficiency, and balance, and then combining these general techniques with specific sports skills. By teaching students at both levels Physical Education Teachers can see carry # overs of their learning, reassess the class curriculum depending on their needs, and, best of all, watch thier growth and development.

Physical educators must obtain certification as teachers. This takes place at a college which has an approved program for the education of PE teachers.

In addition to professional physical education subjects, courses must be undertaken in the arts and sciences. Besides this communication skills, humanities and fine arts; biological sciences; history and social sciences; and natural science and mathematics. Programme requirements such as these attempts to provide the student with a cultural education.

A special experience characterizes the certification program called student teaching. This activity finds the college students, under the supervision of a co-operating teacher and a college faculty member, instructing school students. During this period of intensive training the future teacher practises and refines the skills necessary for practising professional.

More physical educators pursue graduate courses and master's degrees; a few earn doctorates; some obtain graduate degrees in physical education; others undertake work in other areas. The former has three areas of emphasis: motor learning, sport psychology, or motor development. The latter has sub-specialties in anatomy, biomechanics, and exercise physiology. For professional growth and financial reasons, PE teachers are motivated to obtain a master's degree. For those wishing to obtain a position as a PE department chairperson, advanced graduate work is required.

Roles of the Physical Education Teachers

Before choosing a career in Physical education it is essential to know the roles of Physical education teacher. Most of students feel that they are aware of it because they have studied Physical education at various level.

Physical education teacher Should be good at the various levels. The responsibilities of Physical education teacher varied from time to time. As Physical Education teacher one has to play the following roles -

1. As Planner
2. Instruction
3. Record Keeping
4. Equipment Care
5. Faculty Members
6. Counsellor
7. Resource Person
8. Professional.
9. Managing

Chapter - 5

Careers in Coaching

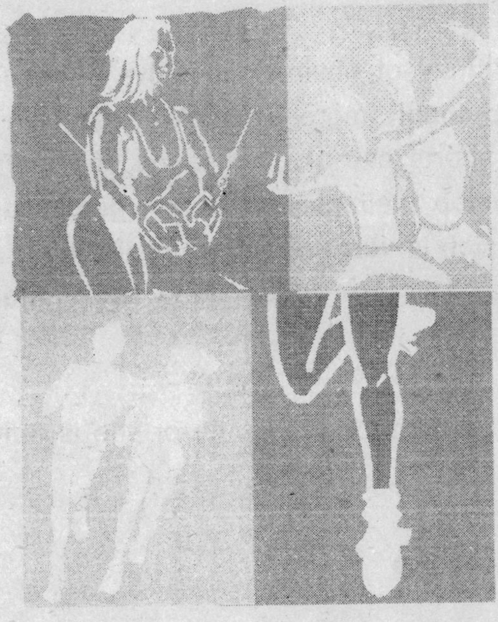

Some students are interested in a career in coaching. In some cases some adopt these career for their part time job alongwith their full time carrers in another area.

Coaching is viewed as very exicting carrer in the modern era as the participation in sport at various level is increasing day by day. Coaches in school, colleges and even in professional institutes are looked upon as important and influential people.

The opportunity of having a positive effect on young people is probably more available in coaching than in any other sports career. Thousands of coaches at all levels, develop their players to win games or events. The profession is very rewarding, challenging, and self-fulfilling; but days are hectic, tiring, and, unfortunately, thankless.

One should not coach unless he or she is familiar with the game.

School Coaches

Assistant Coach

The expansion of minor games and the explosion of women's sports has created a serious need for new persons to enter the profession.

Almost all public and private schools have interscholastic athletic teams which compete against those of other schools. In some states, coaches have taken certain certification courses; in others only certified educators may coach. However, it is possible in both public and private schools to obtain employment.

Is it necessary to be a physical education teachers to serve as a coach? No, most schools would not have enough coaches if this were a policy. In fact, many classroom teachers of various subjects enjoy the variety and involvement with school sports programmes. Many teachers believe that their involvement in school activities with students helps them to be more successful in the classroom.

How can you get started in coaching? As with other careers, you should begin as early as possible.

When you apply for a teaching position, indicate your willingness to serve as a sports coach. In many schools this will aid you to obtain employment. During the interview, express your interest. Most coaches will be only too willing to have an additional assistant if the person has some knowledge, and can provide extra service. Very few head coaches have the time (necessary) to extensively train or monitor an assistant's progress, so the volunteer can be a positive asset rather than a liability.

Most coaches begin their careers serving as assistant coaches, working with teams at the lower levels such as eighth grade, freshman, or junior varsity level. This situation presents a wonderful opportunity gain experience working with young people while experimenting with their own offensive and defensive systems and, most importantly, learning how to teach the sport. Most successful coaches are not only knowledgeable about their sport but have the ability to transfer that knowledge to the players: Most often this ability can be developed in coaching younger players in games played after school an assignment to a team at this level should be looked upon as an opportunity for self-development; it deserves a serious commitment then will be mutually advantageous to you and to the players.

Head Coach

No one aspires to the position of assistant coach; it is a demanding position with recognition. However, your players will realize your ability as will the opposing coaches and your own head coach. Eventually this may result in your promotion to the position from Assistant coach to head coach

Head coaches of varsity teams perform many of the same tasks as their counterparts at lower levels except that they have greater visibility, larger audiences, more responsibility, and, consequently, more accountability. The job is more exciting, rewarding, and glamorous, but the head coach also has greater pressure to be successful.

Duties of Coaching

In the head coaching position there are tremendous time presures-more jobs need to be completed than the outsider may realize.

In addition to preparing for normal teaching duties, head coaches prepares for their coaching. The following are duties of Coaching.

1. Scheduling Discussions.
2. Arranging for pre-season games;
3. Recruiting team managers and statisticians;
4. Meeting with assistant coaches; and giving them guidelines
5. Making a schedule for scouting opponents;
6. Announcing tryouts;
7. Writing press releases for newspapers;
8. Planning for use of athletic facilities;
9. Choosing the team and selecting the starting team;

10. Studying scounting and analyzing your opponents;
11. Creating a game plan;
12. Planning and organizing daily practices;
13. Clipping newspaper stories on your opponents and your team;
14. Inviting the players' parents to the games;
15. Asking knowledgeable persons to scout your team for weaknesses;
16. Arranging for (videotaping) of your team;
17. Encouraging players to attend summer sports camp and participate in summer sports.
18. Attending educational conferences
19. Discussing the program (and problems) with the other administrators;
20. Making the players knowledge up to date through the knowledge of rules and regulation of the game.
21. Writing letters to appropriate individuals;
22. Taking inventory and ordering new equipment

If the above list looks like difficult work, you are right; coaching is not easy. Perhaps the numerous required duties lead many coaches to early retirement. It should be remembered that coaches have regular teaching duties to class preparation, test correction, and course planning) as their primary obligation.

Because of those who leave coaching and the expansion of sports, many opportunies exist for coaching employment.

Coaching, which is really an avocation, offers the opportunity to work very closely with a group of young people and have a very large impact upon their development. Many of the friendships made will be carried throughout the coach's life and provide a continuing source of satisfaction. A coach can make a difference.

Coaching in Universities

College coaching provides high prestige. With this increased status and recognition come significantly greater pressure for success as well as exposure to controversy.

Head coaches command excellent salaries and benefits, have a number of assistant coaches and staff, and frequently have additional opportunities for extra income. Some endorse products, have their own radio or television programs, give presentations, and conduct summer sports camps.

Head coaches of minor sports and coaches at smaller colleges do not enjoy such attention and income. Some are content, not wishing to exchange their situation for the pressure of the limelight.

Head coaches at schools teach physical education courses, though some teach academic subjects or have other responsibilities. They work in the school activities and daily routine.

In addition to having coaching ability, the college coach must have skills that enable her or him to deal with media. Good speaking qualities are essential, Assistant coaches help with many aspects of the job, including one particularly important aspect-recruiting-aiding the head coach with her or his duties.

Much of a university coach's time is spent in convincing young persons to attend her or his college. In many situations, the coach's job depends on a consistent flow of good talent.

If big-time college coaching doesn't sound attractive. Don't despair. Many jobs exist at the community college and small college level. These offer the opportunity to achieve some recognition locally while deriving many of the benefits of coaching.

What opportunites exist for women? A fantastic number of situations are available at the college level for women. Just as women's opportunities have expanded in school coaching, many women's college positions now exist. Several colleges have strongly emphasized women's sports, playing a major schedule of games, publicizing the team, and extensively recruting student/ athletes for scholarships.

Professional Coaching

Professional coaching is generally more pressure-packed at this level, fewer opportunities exist, but those that do provide excellent salaries, benefits, and supportive staffs, Successful coaches work to improve themselves not only during pre-season and the season, but throughout the entire year. This is particularly true of those managing professional teams.

At this stage, job security is most precarious; few seasons pass in which several coaches are not replaced. Persons at this level rarely remain with one team for the entire career.

In addition to handling the normal chores common to all in this position, the technique of motivating highly paid athletes remains a challenge. Coach-player relationships are particularly important in this regard.

Preparing to Coach

If you are interested to prepare career as coach, the following guidlines will help you for preparing yourself.

1. An understanding of the relationship of the interschool programme and the particular sport you are coaching to the total education programme.

2. A knowledge of first aid and the safety practices and techniques pertinent to the sport you are coaching.

3. A thorough knowledge and understanding of the biological, social, moral, emotional, and spiritual values that may accrue from the activity and the best methods of bringing about these desirable outcomes.

4. A knowledge of the most acceptable principles of growth and development and their implications for the sport.

5. An understanding of the basic principles in the care and prevention of injuries together with an understanding of the proper relationship of the coach to the school or team physician.

6. An understanding of the best methods of developing and conditioning members

7. The ability to speak in public of the educational possibilities of the sport.

8. An understanding of the basic psychological principles of motivation, stress, play and group interaction.

9. Knowledge of the fundamentals, offenses, defenses, strategies, and teaching methods involved in a particular sport.

10. A knowledge and sense of responsibility for zonal, state, national and international roles.

The following are suggestions for all those wishing to enter the profession:

1. Begin reading and developing a library of books, articles, and clippings on coaching the sport of your interest.

2. Attend practices of several teams at various levels to observe coaches' organization and teaching technique.

3. Observe as many games, matches, meets as you can. While doing so, become a student of the sport. Observe how a coach performs her or his magic or makes a mistake.

4. Study the rules and rule changes of your sport so that as coach you will be knowledgeable in using the rules for your benefit and that of your team. Strategy frequently revolves around the rules of the game, with opposing coaches working to gain an advantage.

5. Select some coaches that you admire and use them as role models for yourself.

6. Discover what functions sports officials, score keepers, statisticians, and athletic directors perform at an athletic event.

7. Investigate the off-season techniques to develop players in your sport.

8. Attend professional meetings, conferences, and clinics and join the coaching associations related to your sports interest.

9. Regularly Participate in sports.

Coaching can be one of the most positive and wholesome careers our society has to offer. In order to realize these benefits, a tremendous commitment of time and energy will be needed and the earlier you begin the better.

Chapter 6

Sports Officiating

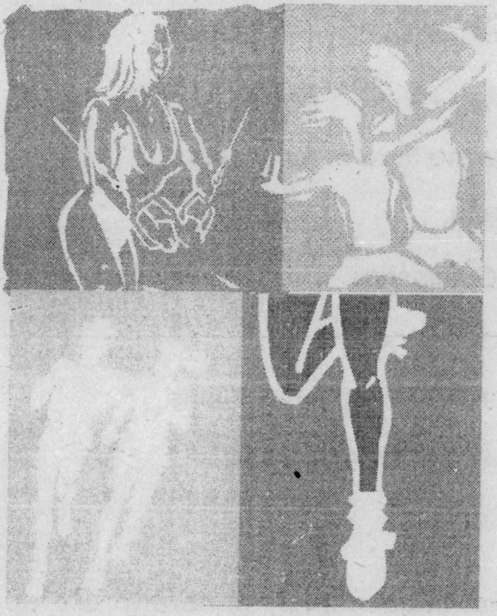

For many years officiating was considered a thankless job where the official took verbal abuse and occasionally physical abuse from the coach, players and crowd. More recently, a growing respect has been noticeable at all levels for the men and women who make the game work by enforcing the rules. This has probably occurred because of growing militancy on the part of the officials, an increase in their skills, and a realization of thier importance and dedication by the public.

The following are guidelines for chosing officiating as career

1. Be Competitive

2. Have Your Head on Right.

3. Get into the Flow of the Game

4. Don't Bark

5. Show Confidence

6. Forget the Fans

7. Answer Reasonable Questions

8. Choose Your Words Wisely

9. Stay Cool

The above suggestions, generally are applicable to officiating at all levels, may need slight modification in special situations, as a whole they provide excellent guidelines. A command over the rules is an important part of being a truly successful official. But establishing and maintaining rapport with coaches as well as players the official should avoid getting in to potentially difficult situations.

What kind of person makes a good sports official? Some of these personality characteristics are tolerance, self-confidence, and the ability to make decisions under stress; taking decisions at the flick of the Eyelid give officiating a try.

Officiating in Schools

Most officials became introduced to their profession by a friend or through participation in sports, many future officials will probably enter their careers as a result of attendance at a school. Naturally, the official's associations will provide a training program for their new recruits; The schools, however, represent an in-depth concentrated approach to learning the officials' art.

The specific purpose is to supply supervised training for young people to qualify for umpire positions in professional college.

Preparing for your Future

If officiating is potentially your career, pursue these suggestions;

1. Read about your future profession

2. Volunteer to officiate, wherever you can find an opportunity.

3. Study and master the rules for your sport.

4. Stay aware of recent changes, interpretations, and emphasis:

5. Participate to the extent you are able in the sport of your interest.

6. Work to develop the personality trais of an official, such as independence, maturity, self-confidence, and a high-moral character.

Chapter - 7

Sports Administration

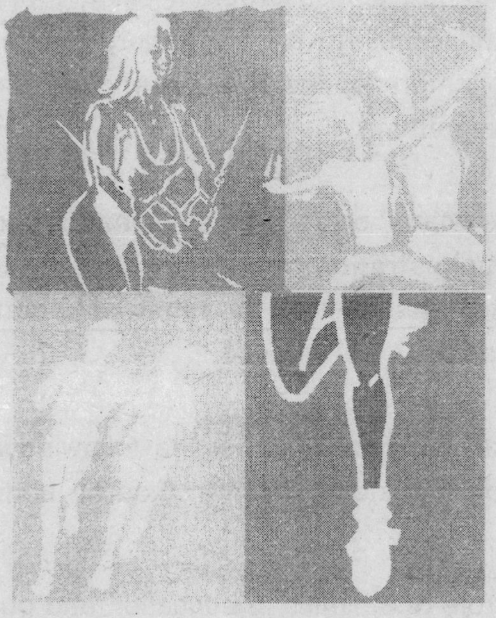

The expansion of sports has seen a corresponding rise in the number of persons necessary to co-ordinate and manage the various programmes.

The successful operation of most organized sport programme requires some degree of administrative leadership. As the scope of a program is increased, the degree of administrative responsibilities also increases.

Where ever the sports program exist, there exists a need for individuals to fullfill a variety of administrative roles. The nature of the role depend on the need of specific programme.

There are many opportunities available to work in sports administration, in universities, colleges and schools too, as well as in other associations and organizations.

Professional organizations list the following abilities in athletic administrators. These include an understanding of:

1. The role of athletics in education and our society.
2. The rules, regulations, policies, and procedures of the various governing bodies.
3. Sound business procedures as related to athletic administraion

4. Administrative problems as related to equipment and supplies.

5. Problems related to facilities, indoor and outdoor.

6. School law and liability

7. The factors involved in the conduct of athletic events.

8. Good public relation techniques.

9. Staff relationships

10. The health aspects of athletics

11. The psychological and sociological aspects of sports.

A successful athletic director requires many important personality traits such as,

1. Leadership
2. A sincere interest in youth and their development
3. A sense of humor
4. Even temperament
5. Optimism
6. A sense of justice and impartiality
7. Integrity and solidarity

Professional and other Positions

Many opportunities exist for positions of administration. Not all of these are top level positions; many people serve in supportive roles directing specific aspects of a programme.

Chapter 8

Professional Athletes

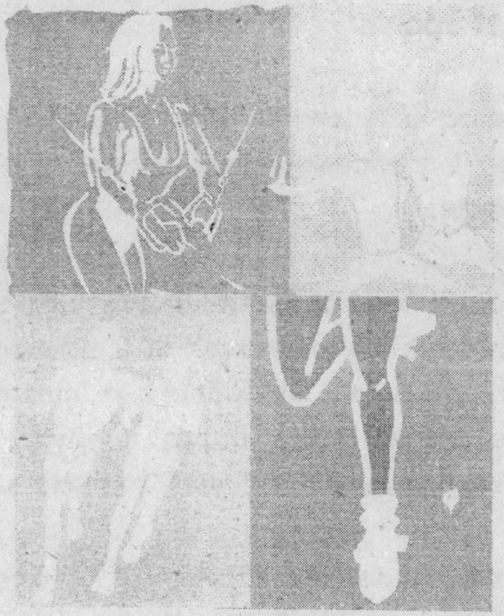

Invariably every body at some time or other has entertained the fantasy of becoming a professional athlete. A wide variety of sports exists from which to choose to prepare oneself. Regardless of the sport(s) chosen, it will be a long, rigorous battle that will test the physical skills and character of aspiring athlets. Only those with great desire and intensity, meshed with the appropriate physical and mental skills, will enter the select circle. The road remains difficult, but the rewards make it worthwhile.

The Value of Sports

For many years athletics has been justified in schools and society. It provides for the physical development of young people.

Physical education specialists have neglected to secure converts to the objectives of their programme. Perhaps their traditional involvement in interscholastic athletics has drained their energies, depriving them of communicating the values of fitness and sports.

Despite some wonderfully successful activities there are far too many young people who have not profited from good health and fitness.

Some studies undertaken in the area of youth fitness have showed dramatic gains for students clearly, schools, communities, social and professional organizations, and, most importantly, families, need to give more attention to youth fitness.

A wave of interest in fitness has spread in India's adult community.

To some extent this reinterest in fitness has come from what has come to be known as the "new' fitness. This orientation emphasizes a mental, spiritual, and physical approach characterized by non-competitiveness and fun. Similarly, many young people want to preserve their bodies and remain youthful through exercise.

Sports involvement makes a major contribution to the physical well-being of the participants.

Sports has the potential to build character among the youth. That is, the self-discipline, teamwork, and fair play so much a part of sports teaches character skills, Generally, with a growing number of noticeable exceptions, sports has done this. It provides preparation for life or life adjustment. There are good times when everything goes exactly right for the players and the team. There are also stretches of terrible lows when nothing goes right. Sports participation permits the athlete to experience adversity, something many young people in affluent rarely encounter. The highs and lows involved in sports offer an excellent preparation for life's stresses and struggles.

Preparation for Career.

Professional athletes know it but often those aspiring to become professional do not: that is, almost life-long preparation is necessary prior to playing professional sports.

The Six D'S:-

1. Discipline - The ability to take discipline from others as well as self discipline is the first step to success.

2. Desire to excel - This motivation exists as a must, not only for ball players but everyone. In addition, this means getting the most out of every practice.

3. Determination - The desire to keep on trying regardless of setbacks such as a bad play or an injury.

4. Dedication - A commitment to your goal that carries with it the sacrifice that is necessary for success.

5. Dependability - Reliability and consistency is the mark of the "pro." Coaches must know that a player can be counted upon to contribute in many situations. It also means the small things, such as being on time for the bus leaving for the game and manifesting responsibility when given a job to perform.

6. Darn it, anyway - When everything seems against you and nothing seems to work, do something - but don't give up. Some times an action disrupts the harmony or flow of your opponent permitting you to reverse the situation.

Women Involvement

The national and international success of women's athletics has captured the attention. Just a decade and a half ago female athletes were thought too frail to participate in sports to the extent they do today. Athletics was believed to be too demanding and too intense except for men.

The myth that women cannot engage in conditioning and training activities is very quickly disappearing.

1. One can be athletically skilled and trained rigorously without any loss of feminity.

2. The female is capable of performing strenuous activity without any physiological impairment.

3. Active females possess a better state of health than those who are inactive.

4. The female is capable of high level motor tasks as well as those involving endurance capacities.

5. Strength can be developed or improved in the female at a higher ratio than that of the male.

The training needs of females are basically the same as for males and there is no reason to invent separate training techniques for females.

Women recieve more injuries than men but that is due to improper handling of equipment & lack of proper training facilites.

The injuries incurred by women, concluded that improper training methods, and lack of modern training methods are major factors in women's injuries. It is suggested screening programs to identify poorly conditioned athletes; pre-season, in-season,and post-season training using weights; and earlier participation.

Opportunities for women in athletics have expanded greatly, at all levels.While there exists some debate over certain aspects of conditioning and training, most coaches and trainers agree on the main emphasis weight training, endurance, agility, stretching and running for speed, and cardiovascular with a knowledgeable person as to procedures so as to maximize her or his efforts and to avoid injury. Weight conditioning brings gains of strength and power, reduces injuries, and builds confidence, while some opportunities exist at school gyms or health clubs owning your personal set of free weights will offer increased opportunities to work out.

Mental Preparation

Few make it to only athletic success unless they have a "sound mind" to accompany the "sound body", It means unless a team has smart guards that can analyze changing defenses, break presses, and control the tempo of the game, it has little chance of making it to the state tournament. Today's sports are a sophisticated business - the person who doesn't make it in the classroom will have serious difficulties on the court or field. Research tells us that athletes as a group outperform their fellow students in academics.

In the past, some athletes have obtained the stigma of dullards. Today's coaches avoid players who has a poor academic record because that student will have eligibiltiy problems as well as difficulty understanding offensive and defensive systems. As sports become more complex, the mental power of athletes also needs to keep pace accordingly. Remember, doing well in the classroom will contribute to your athletic performance.

Mental Toughness

A positive mental attitude remains a must for success in athletics. Players must rise above the adversity of a particular situation to become successful. The inexperienced player will compound a mistake by making another mistake.

The true test of a winning attitude comes late in a game. Winners make those plays - they want the ball - they know they can do it. Losers think of excuses, prefer not to be in the game, wish the ball would not come to them. Winning and losing become habits. Make winning your habit.

Nutrition

Good nutrition and supplementation with vitamins and minerals is obvious. Prospective athletes must remain particularly cautious of their food consumption.

A seven-mile run prior to breakfast

Lunch (high protein)

Swimming

Tennis

Dinner

Workout

Combining with rest, relaxation, sleep, and physical training with a proper nutritional plan, and a sense of self confidence will aid you in the direction of athletic success.

In considering your future as a professional athlete, work hard to make it to the top, and act like you don't have a second chance. Remember it is better to have tried and not succeeded than never to have tried at all.

In addition to a continuing commitment to improving yourself and giving time and service back to the society that supports you, prepare for the day your career ends. For most players, the transition from the glory and the limelight back to "ordinary" life is difficult enough; it should not be compounded by financial problems or anxiety related to job. With proper preparation, most athletes can use sports as a springboard to a fine second career. Many opportunities exist in sports; in addition, business and industry often seek out athletes for employment.

Guidelines for Professional Sports

1. Know all about your game / sport
2. Plan your physical development
3. Practice makes a man perfect so continue with practice.
4. Make a planned diet, for yourself which will help your development and growth.
5. Build self confidence and positive mental attitude.
6. Be a winner not only in sport but in life too.

Chapter 9

Sports Medicine

The explosion of injuries at all levels and a desire by players, parents, and coaches to reduce them has created a greatly expanded need for sports medicine personnel.

Historically, sports medicine personnel have concern with athletes only after an injury. Now strong emphasis has been placed upon injury avoidance. This takes place largely through conditioning:-

Rights of Athletes

1. Proper Conditioning helps to prevent injuries by hardening the body and increasing resistance to fatigue.

1. Are prospective players given directions and activities for pre-season conditioning?

2. There a minimum of two weeks of practice before the first game or contest?

3. Each player is required to warm up thoroughly prior to participation?

4. Substituions are made without hesitation when players evidence disability?

2. Careful Coaching leads to skillful performance, which lowers the incidence of injuries.

1. Emphasis is given to safety in teaching technique and elements of play?

2. Injuries are carefully analyzed to determine causes and suggest preventive programs?

3. Tactics are discouraged that may increase the hazards and thus the incidence of injuries?

4. Practice period is carefully planned and of reasonable duration?

3. Good Officiating promotes enjoyment of the game as well as the protection of players.

1. Players as well as coaches are thoroughly schooled in the rules of the games?

2. Rules and regulations are strictly enforced in practice periods as well as in games?

3. Officials are employed who are qualified both emotionally and technically for their responsibilites?

4. Right Equipment and Facilities serve a unique purpose in protection of players.

1. The best protective is equipment provided for contact sports?

2. Careful attention is given to proper fitting and adjustment of equipment?

3. Equipment is properly maintained, and are worn and out-moded items discarded?

4. Proper areas for play are provided and carefully maintained?

5. Adequate Medical Care is a necessity in the prevention and control of athletic injuries.

1. There is a thorough pre-season health history and medial examination?

2. A physician is present at contests and readily available during practice sessions?

3. The physician makes the decision as to whether an athlete should return to play following injury during games or not?

4. Authority from a physician is required before an athlete can return to practice after being out of play because of disabling injury?

5. The care is given to athletes by coach or trainer limited to first aid and medically prescribed services?

The importance of proper conditioning involving strength, cardio-vascular fitness, and flexibilty cannot be over-emphasized. Principles of Athletic Conditioning that every coach, player, and sports medicine professional must know and implement.

1. Warm up - each activity must be preceded by an adequate warm up. Stretching activities and running will provide the greatest benefit. Warming down likewise requires attention.

2. **Gradualness** - start slowly with conditioning and look to peak. Setting goals can be helpful.

3. **Timing** - Athlets must be counseled not to overdo workouts; relaxation and rest form part of every conditioning program.

4. **Intensity** - workouts and practices must be characterized by quality and continuous activity with appropriate rest periods.

5. **Capacity level** - while being cautious to avoid the above pitfalls, athletes will want to work to capacity and should have the encouragement to do so.

6. **Strength** - greater endurace, speed, flexibility, and confidence will result from improved strength.

7. **Motivation** - sports medicine personnel can reinforce the coaches' techniques to stimulate players.

8. **Specialization** - A must in each player's conditioning programme exercises to improve the player in relation to the sport he or she wishes to play and give time and improve his # her weakness.

9. Relaxation - trainers should familiarize themselves with specific techniques to teach players how to relax and thereby recover from tension, fatigue, and stress.

10. Routine - a planned daily, weekly, and monthly routine must be constructed for each player in co-operation with the athlete and coach.

The above principles should serve as guidelines. Careful adherance can make an important difference to athletes. Consequently, it's a must for players to warm up even if they are late, and practice has already begun.

Athletic Trainers

An athletic trainer's duties consists of the implementation of an injury prevention programme, and the initiation of immediate treatment and rehabilitation procedures for the injured athlete as directed by the team physician. He or she is the person you see down on the field or sitting on the bench close to the large first aid kit. Long before the contest, the trainer has prepared the participants, taping and providing therapy for others. He or she will stay after the game, providing services as needed.

Trainers engage in the following activities

1. Designing and monitoring a program of conditioning in co-operation with the coaching staff.

2. Supervision of safety factors involving playing areas.

3. Selection of proper equipment in co-operation with the coaching staff and equipment manager (see below)

4. Administration of first aid to injured athletes.

5. Applicaiton of devices such as braces and bandages to prevent injury.

6. Development and supervision of the rehabilitation program, for an injured athlete under the supervision of a physician. Often the trainer will make sure that the athlete exercises to prevent a recurring injury and then monitor the improvement of muscle strength.

7. Maintainance of the athletic training area and performance of such tasks as ordering supplies, supervising the servicing of equipment, and keeping careful records.

8. Development of good working relationships with the players, coaches, physicians, and with the school authorities or professional management.

The duties and obligations are quite significant and the athletic trainer's importance to sports continues to increase. The most important role of the trainer is to prevent an injury from occuring, participation in the activities is playing for the Eagles team! A sense of commitment of the team is Essential for the trainer, the greatest satisfaction comes from seeing an athlete return to maximum potential by performing well after an injury.

Another area of recent concern is that of injury prevention as related to equipment selection. The trainer works as a member of a team composed of the coach and equipment manger and is guided by the follwing in choosing equipment:

1. Its specifications must provide maximum protection for the area to be protected.

2. It should be able to withstand repeated use with a decrease in efficiency.

3. It should fit carefully so that it can provide protection under playing conditions.

4. It must not impede the player's activity (as nearly as possible).

5. It must not create a hazard to other contestants. States and leagues usually have a rule against this.

6. It must be replaced when it is no longer effective and has lost its protective value.

Once you believe that you have the physical and psychological qualities to become an athletic trainer, begin by taking science-related courses in high school (health, chemistry, etc.). Association (see address below). In college you will take both liberal arts (English, history, science) and professional education subjects.

Sports Physician

At the center of the sports medicine profession are the sports medicine physicians - othopedists, osteopaths, and chiropractors,

The following are the basic requirement for team Physican physical characteristics and defects predisposing the player to injury especially in the collision sports. The physical examination should include determination of the individual's maturiy, balance, co-ordination, agility, stamina, and strength.

3. The physician must know the basic fundamentals of the particular sport with which he or she is involved, to better understand the mechanism of the injuries occuring, as well as the injured participant and her or his problem.

4. The physican must observe and evaluate the emotional well-being of the athlete, especially the young player. If the candidate is being pushed by a frustrated parent to be a superstar or made apprehensive by a parent because he or she might get hurt?

5. The physician should fit and select all protective gear and equipment and check it as to type and quality.

6. The physician should supervise the trainer or the coach in the proper use of physiotherapeutic techniques used in the training room, the physician is responsible for conditioning and rehabilitation exercise. (such as weight training)

Upon the doctor rests the responsibility for total rehabilitaion of the injured athlete (mental and physical), a careful examination must precede before returning to participation.

7. The physician must advise the coach not to teach dangerous blocking and checking practices and the avoidance of mismatches between athletes, especially young players.

8. The physician (or a designated replacement) must be available at all times to examine the injured player as soon as possible after the injury. This is especially true in collision sports where, if possible, the physician should be on the field.

9. The physician must prevent an injured player from returning to the game if there exists a reasonable doubt about his condition.

10. The Physician must obtain x-rays of injuries (and other information as necessary) prior to judging the condition of the injury.

Orthopedist

While some teams employ general practitioners (GPs) in the capacity of sports physicians, orthopedists by their training best serve in this position. Orthopedists are medical doctors (MDs) who treat injuries to the skeletal system - backs, necks, arms, legs and joints, and to the body's muscles. Those involved in sports normally serve on a consulting basis with teams and / or work in sports clinics.

Osteopath

Osteophathic physicians (DOs) concentrate on the muscular skeletal system of the body in returning the injured athlete to action. As do medical doctors (MDs), they utilize surgery, drugs, and other acceptable health care practices. In addition, they may use manipulation and emphasize the treatment of the whole athlete in designing a conditioning or rehabilitation programme.

Chiropractor

As with osteopaths a small percent of chiropractors serve in a consulting capacity to sports teams. Doctors of Chiropractic emphasize the utilization of manipulation (adjustments) as their primary treatment. They do not believe in using prescription drugs or surgery nor are they permitted to do so by state law. Chiropractors do employ other treatments with the injured athlete - heat, water, massage therapy, and others.

Individuals considering a career as a sports physician should realize the academic commitment. Excellent grades and an interest and competence in science remains a must.

If you're planning a career in this area, a long commitment to academics is necessary. In addition, these specialties, require passing a licensure examination to practise medicine in the state of your choice.

Sports physicians have a strong interest in improving their profession; many conduct research on various aspects of athletic performance. In addition these individuals work well with people and have a strong interest in athletics and sports.

Physical Therapy

Physical therapists work with athletes who have been disabled through accident, birth defect, or illness. Some therapists work with athletes sent to them by a physician, to aid in the rehabilitation of an injury. Treatments include (1) exercises for increasing strength, endurance, coordination, and range of motion; (2) activities to facilitate motor capacity or learning;

(3) instruction in activities of daily living and use of assistance devices; and (4) application of physical agents such as heat and cold, sound, water, and acupuncture to relieve pain and/or alter physiological status.

Physical therapists attend college to receive certification in their profession; some attend graduate programs and enter leadership positions in the field.

Many physical therapists who work with athletes do so at sports medicine clinics where they assist other professional in rehabilitating athletes.

Sports Medicine Clinics and Centers

In recent years there has been an expanded interest in the team approach to the prevention and treatment of athletic injuries. The previous information on the athletic trainers, sports physicians, and physical therapists emphasized the importance of these individuals working together. In accordance with this team concept, there is a strong trends toward injured athletes being treated at sports medicine clinics or centers. Most often these exist in one of three settings: at universities related to medical school, at hospitals, and as private enterprises in medical buildings.

As sports medicine clinics and centers expand, they will be an important source of employment for athletic trainers, physical therapists, and physicians. They offer more flexibility in terms of activities traditionally found in these careers.

Sports medicine professionals make an important contribution to athletics; all sports enthusiasts deserve to give these occupations serious consideration when choosing a career.

Getting Started

1. Maintain the training room and the supplies.
2. Aids with the taping and treatments.
3. Prepare field kits and be available during contests tournament and practices.
4. Reporting new injuries to the coach and trainer.
5. Preparing a beverage and having it ready for athletes' breaks during games and practices
6. Complete a course for student trainers.
7. Keep student trainer duties separate from student manager responsibilities.
8. Aid in record keeping of player injuries and treatment.
9. Perform related tasks as asked by coach, trainer, or physician.

10. Maintain professional rapport with players, coaches, physician, trainer, and with opposing team and its personnel.

Many colleges and high schools utilize female student athletic trainers. Excellent career opportunities exist for women athletic trainers.

The strong desire from all segments of society and the sports world to curtail athletic injuries will insure varied, interesting, and profitable career opportunities in sports medicine in the future.

Chapter 10

Sports Journalism

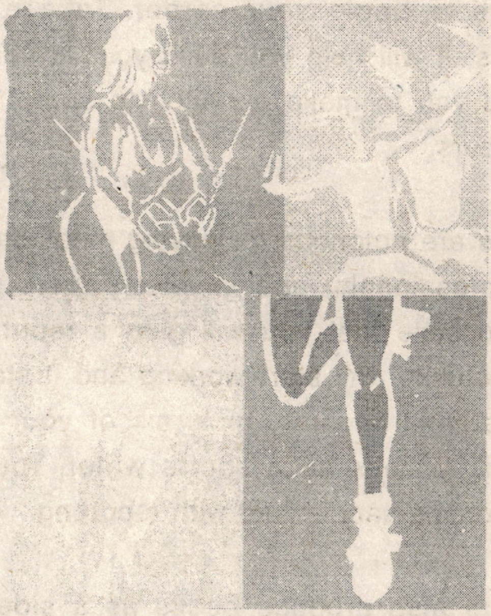

Most of the student want to enter the exciting world of broadcasting and print journalism. Public visability, very good salary, and the opportunity to be in on the action attracts people to these positions. The most exciting of journalism careers involve sports and athletics.

Preparing for your Career

Many opportunities exist on school and college newspapers to begin your career. Take a position writing news; it will help you build your craft of writing and will aid you to make a switch to sports when an opening occurs.

Newspapers are notorious for paying mediocre salaries to their professionals, and smaller papers pay even less. It's possible that you will gain a reputation and your own column will start working and it start paying you a substantial income. In terms of your career, it marks your success as a sports writer. Your column would be commentary, mixed with reporting.

Most writers also produce books as a sideline. This serves as a creative outlet for their talents as well as an additional source of income. A considerable market exists for sports books, and publishers look for manuscripts.

Reporters began their careers as copy aides helping around the office by performing clerical tasks. This would involve small, unspectacular assignments eventually leading up to important tasks. If you plan such a career, include several courses in writing; grammer skills will be a necessity. You should also consider a strong background in the humanities and using your free electives in sports courses from the physical education programme. Courses in photography will increase your chances of obtaining a job,

In recent years, the expansion of television and radio coverage of sporting events has resulted in a modification of newspaper coverage. A decline in straight factual reporting and an increase in features has occurred. Not only does the reader want to know what happended, but such additional information as the condition of the player injured, who might be traded, and the likelihood of the success against the next opponent. Some outstanding features have resulted from careful excellent investigative research revealing serious abuses in sports. However, most are interviews with an athlete answering a series of questions about an aspect of her or his career.

A newspaper writer at this point in time has a very special obligation to society to remain vigilant for excesses that may destroy sports. Coaches have forced injured players to participate; athletic directors have condoned illegal recruiting; players have put their own importance above that of their team and their sport; youth league managers have played only to win;

and coaches have publicly abused players for mistakes.

Opportunities exist for well-prepared and knowledgeable candidates. Sometimes it's glamorous, usually it's exciting, but it's very hard work; even the writers considered the best in the country will tell you that it took years of dedicated effort to develop their craft.

Sportscaster

The Sports World gives as much attention to well-known sports personalities from the broadcast media as they do to some athletes. The glamour usually surrounds the television announcers great visibility.

Television announcers receive the best salaries and the greatest exposure to the public. Although they may apppear on the show only twice a day for four or five minutes, they spend most of the day preparing for their air time. Often this involves attending press conferences, interviewing players, and covering games. It's an exciting life that brings the sportscaster in close contact with the sports. In addition to very good speaking ability, writing skills are also essential since sportscasters compose the information they announce.

Closely related to the television news position is that of the radio newscaster.This job requires excellent knowledge of almost all sports, as a broadcaster frequently is "on the spot. Most of-time will often find broadcasters attending games. In addition to their shows they usually handle sports news for their station:

They provide insights to certain techniques and strategies the coach or athlete may employ; he or she will often provide amusing anecdotes about players. Most recently there has been an attempt to carefully put together a team of announcers that will complement each other's abilities and contribute to the listener's enjoyment of the game. Many hours are spent by the staff in preparing for a game or event. Reading of players' backgrounds, talking with coaching staffs, and meeting with public relations specialists help in this regard.

Knowledge of sports and an excellent speaking voice is a very important prerequisite for the sports-caster's career; physical attractiveness looms important for the television positions. and the knowledge of games. It is useful to take many of the same courses suggested for newspaper and public relations careers, such as writing, public speaking, sport studies and physical education. Similarly, try to become involved in sports at some level of activity.

The increasing channels in Television and Radio has made this carrer a great potential.

Chapter 11

Alternative Career

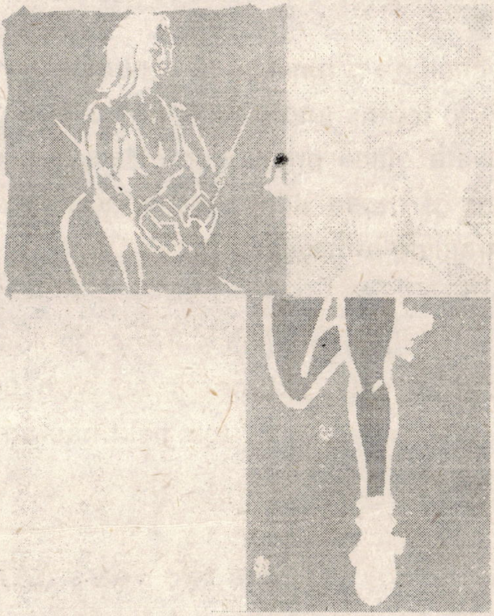

Sports Psychologist

Sports psychologists utilize their knowledge of human behaviour to assist athletes and teams to maximize their performance. The pressure of big-time athletics at the college and professional levels (and sometimes even the high school level) can lead to problems. Pressure situations may lead to physical and psychological difficulties among coaches, officials, administrators, and athletes.

Sports psychologists function in a number of ways - as consultants to teams and clinics, as college professors, and as private office practioners. However, only about ten percent of those acting as sports psychologists have had training in psychology!

As more individuals educated in psychology become available, they will replace those with inadequate backgrounds. Consequently, this field has ample career opportunities.

Sports psychology requires two years (M.A.) to four years (Ph.D) training beyond four years of college. Excellent grades are a must. Most pursuing this major will try to mesh it with some electives in sports studies and/or athletic training to increase their understanding of the sports world.

Sports Photographer - Still and Motion

Sports photographers capture on film action and the beauty of sports. A good sports photographer possesses excellent skills developed through many years of experience. If this sounds too demanding, consider beginning your career by "shooting" an amateur competiting with a small instamatic photographic camera or an inexpensive cartridge motion picture or video camera. If your interest develops, puchase more sophisticated equipment. Many local newspapers and school yearbooks need photographs; ask them if they would like some of yours. Many schools film and videotape athletic events for students, players, and coaches to review. This may be an opportunity to gain some experience while aiding the school.

Some photographers work for specific magazines or newspapers. If these are general publications, the photography staff will cover subjects other than sports; while a few photographers may specialize in athletics, they are called upon to work on other assignments. Naturally, those employed by sports magazines or newspapers would only work in athletics.

A significant number of photographers in this field work as freelancers. This means they are self-employed and work for a number of publications. Some receive specific assignments to cover particular events and will sell the "shots" they take. Others work part-time for a couple of newspapers, supplying them with several photographs a week. Others may attend games and hope they will get some photos of a spectacular event to sell to a magazine or newspaper.

Very few opportunities exist for sports photographers; however, a small group do very well financially combining excellent salaries with a glamorous life. You may wish to consider it an avocation (hobby) or an enjoyable second job. If you think you're interested, start now. Buy a camera and take a photography, film, or video course in an evening school.

Agents and Sports Representatives

In this era of fantastic salaries for professional athletes, the agent has become a visible member of the sports scenes. Agents, sometimes called representatives, act as the players' intermediaries with the team's owner and general manager, to secure the best financial and playing arrangement for the athlete. The use of agents occurs in several professions:

Agents are usually lawyers or accountants. They obtain their salary as a percentage of the income the player will receive from the team (or athletic event, as in boxing). Agents normally receive ten percent for their negotiation of the contract.

In addition to negotiating contracts, many serve as financial agents for players, making suggestions for investments, product endorsements, and handling income taxes. Some act as representatives for organizations such as the football players or for baseball umpires. In doing so, they work to obtain better salaries, retirement benefits, and improved working conditions.

For many years, players made their own arrangements with team owners. With the introduction of television, rivalries between leagues, and the expansion of players' legal rights, salaries accelerated greatly. Many athletes in past years were underpaid for the performance; today some players are grossly overpaid. Hopefully a leveling of salaries will occur before sports is seriously damaged in terms of public support.

Opportunities for agents in the future will remain small and the salaries will continue to be excellent. If you're interested, the best background is law or accountng. For law, this means four years of college in which you must do well academically and then three years of law school. Accounting will require undergraduate school. While in school, association with sports as a player, writer, or broadcaster will provide excellent experience.

Health and Fitness Specialists

The growth of health clubs and spas, the development of an interest in industry and business in fitness, and an expanded awareness by retirement homes and communities concerning the relationship of exercise and good health has resulted in a need for individuals trained in these areas.

Normally health and fitness specialists have come from the ranks of physical education teachers and individuals with an interest in fitness (weight trainers, joggers, aerobic dances, martial arts followers). However, as this field becomes more specialized and important, the next generation of these career specialists will come largely from the ranks of exercise physiologists.

Health clubs and spas employ a wide variety of individuals with an interest in fitness. Most do not have special training; however, some of the larger, more expensive clubs employ an exercise specialist. This person would train the other employees, organize the fitness program, and assist members that want advice on health and fitness.

Sports Marketing

The Budget on Sports promotion is increasing day by day and many companies and Industries spend large amount in the promotion of sports. Some adopt some

Particular game and spend lot of money. Equipments, clothing, supplies and use of sports facilities are being purchased at a continually increasing rate. Carrer in Sports marketing includes the product sale, selling of rights for particular game or event, getting sponsorship for an event etc. Sports marketing too is very challenging career.

Sports Scientists

Sports Scientists study the effects of sports & exercise on the human body in order to know the importance of Fitness & Well-being. To be a good Sports Scientists, the scientific background and interests in sports is required. Sports scientists work in the field of academic research, which includes, bromechanics, physishomy, psychology, statictics and kinesishony, Even Sports scientist work on a very specific topic in the area of sports & Physical Education. The job opportunity for Sports Scientists is available all around the world. Sports Federation, Govt Institutes, Research Centers, are on look out for good sports scientists.

Sports Massage Therapist

Becoming a good massage therapists require dedication, hardwork, Perception and practice, there is no such qualification required to start with, but one needs to learn anatomy and Physiology. With this one can become confident at touching and handling. The sports Massage therapist require a wide range of knowledge and skills about anatomy & Physiology, effects of exercise an human # body, of massage, First aid, injury management and massage techniques and how to apply them on each part of body. In the modern era the career as sports massae therapist is becoming important and large number of job opportunities in public as well as well in private sector is available.

Sports Facilities Maintaince Personal

This is relatively a new field. It does not require any professional qualification but it requires dedication and hardwork and the knowledge of various games and activities. Most employees learn their skills on the Job itself. However some positions such as maintaining playfields, equipment's, and supervision for work, requires specific knowledge. The person with a diploma in recreation and sports management have better scope. The Job opportunities for this position is available in public and private undertakings.

Stadium Administrator

While few opportunities are available in this field and experience of many position is required . This too is very attractive position and career in modern world. The knowledge and experience along with dedication of hardwork is required. As stadium Administrator you are responsible for every movement in the stadium.

Statistician

The role of computer has emerged as a weapon in the arsenal, the data supplied by the computer adds to coach's knowledge to make his strategy of play and information can help in decision making. Statastics are kept at most level of play. Career as statisticians are limited, however several, opportunities do exist to follow this job as avocation. The developing skills in this area are beneficial in related areas such as sports information, newspaper career and as record keeper.

Groundsman

It is a fact that sports people only remember the pitches on which they play, but not the person who prepared and maintain the ground to play. The opportunities in this field are growing day by day, with the development of sports in the country. It is highly skilled job and need practical experience. There is no such courses in the country but the job opportunities are avaiable. The groundsman should have the knowledge of wheather, soils, turf and other ingredients of the ground. Dedication in this job can make him more important. There is a shortage of skilled groundsman, and job opportunities as part and fulltime groundsman are avaiable at various level.

Appendix

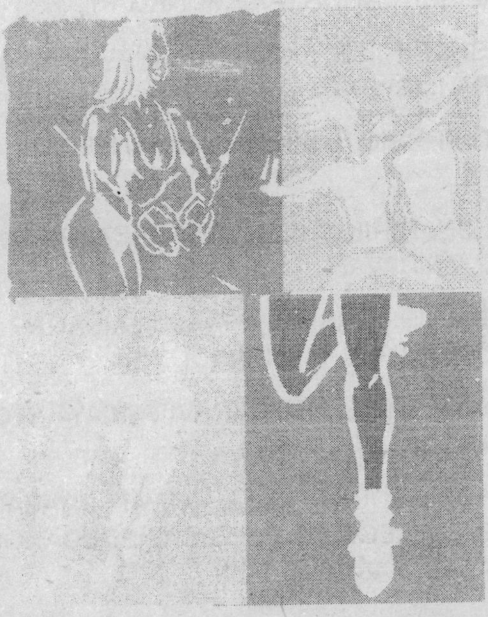

LIST OF UNIVERSITIES AND COLLEGES OFFERING VARIOUS COURSES IN PHYSICAL EDUCATION AND SPORTS SCIENCES

- A.P. SPORTS SCHOOL, SECUNDERABAD.
- ACADEMY OF YOGA CONSCIOUSNESS, CHAITANYARAMAM, VIGINIGIRI–535250 DISTT. VIZIANAGRAM (A.P)
- ACHRAYA NARENDER DEV KISHAN P.G. COLLEGE, BABHAN.
- ADARSH PHYSICAL TEACHER TRAINING SCHOOL, SUROTH.
- AHEMADNAGAR ZILLA M. P. S'S COLLEGE OF PHYSICAL EDUCATION, AHEMDNAGAR
- AMBIKA SHARIRIK SHIKSHAN MAHAVIDYALAYA, BHANDARA (MS)
- AMRAVATI PHYSICAL EDUCATION COLLEGE, AMRAVATI (BPED)
- AMRAVTI SHARIRIK SHIKSHAN PRASARAK MANDALS COLLEGE, AMRAVATI.
- ANNAMALAI UNIVERSITY, ANNAMALAINAGAR - 608 002 DISTT. CUDDALORE, TAMIL NADU.
- ARYA KANYA SHIKSHAN MAHAVIDYALAYA, ITOLA, DISTT. BARODA.
- ASHVAGHOSH EDUCATION & VYAYAM PRASARAK MANDAL'S COLLEGE OF PHYSICAL EDUCATION, AURANGABAD – 431 004 (MS)
- AWADESH PRATAP SINGH UNIVERSITY, REWA- 486 003, MADHYA PARDESH
- AYKKS COLLEGE OF PHYSICAL EDUCATION, (BPED) DHULE (NORTH MS)

- B. K. PATIL COLLEGE OF PHYSICAL EDUCATION, BULDHANA. (MS)
- B. K. PATIL SHARIRIK SHIKSHAN MAHAVIDYALAYA, MALKAPUR (MS)
- B. P. ED COLLEGE, NEHRU NAGAR, SOLAPUR (MS)
- B. P. ED COLLEGE, SATARA (MS)
- B. SHAMSUNDER PHYSICAL EDUCATION COLLEGE, GULBARGA (KARNATAKA)
- BABA SAHEB DR. BHIM RAO AMBEDKAR COLLEGE OF PHYSICAL EDUCATION, ARTONI. AGRA. (U.P)
- BABASAHEB GHARPHALKAR SHARIRIK SHIKSHAN MAHAVIDYALAYA; (BPED) PULGAON-442 302 (MS)
- BABASAHEB PARANJAPE COLLEGE OF PHYSICAL EDUCATION, BEED. (MS)
- BABURAM DESHMUKH SHARIRIK SHIKSHAN MAHAVIDYALAYA, NAGPUR. (MS)
- BACHELOR OF PHYSICAL EDUCATION COLLEGE, YAVATMAL. (MS)
- BALIAPAL COLLEGE OF PHYSICAL EDUCATION, (BPED/ MPED) BALIAPAL, (ORISSA)
- BALKAVI THOMBRE COLLEGE OF PHYSICAL EDUCATION, (BPED), BORADI-425 448 (NORTH MS)
- BARKATULLAH VISHWAVIDYALAYA, BHOPAL - 462 026, MADHYA PARDESH
- BASAVESHESHWAR PHYSICAL EDUCATION COLLEGE, BAGALKOT (KARNATAKA)
- BBA COLLEGE, DHARMSALA (HIMACHAL PRADESH)
- BEYNON-SMITH PHYSICAL EDUCATION COLLEGE, BELGAUM (KARNATAKA)

- BHAGWAN CHAKRADHAR SWAMI SHARIRIK SIKSHAN MAHAVIDYALAYA, (BPED), TALODI-441221. (MS)
- BHAGWAN SHRI CHAKRADHAR SWAMI COLLEGE OF PHY.EDUCATION, CHANDRAPUR.
- BHARAT MATA PHYSICAL TEACHER TRAINING SCHOOL, KISHANGANJ.
- BHARATHIAR UNIVERSITY, COIMBATORE - 641046, TAMIL NADU
- BHARATHIDASAN UNIVERSITY, PALKALAIPERUR, TIRUCHINAPALLI–620024 (TN)
- BHARTI VIDYAPEETH'S DEEMED UNIVERSITY COLLEGE OF PHYSICAL EDUCATION, DHANAKWADI, PUNE-411043. (MS)
- BHAURAO PATIL BAPAT SHARIRIK SHIKSHAN MAHAVIDYALAYA, (BPED), RAJURA. (MS)
- BHAVNAGAR UNIVERSITY, BHAVNAGAR 364002, GUJRAT
- BHUPAL NOBLE'S COLLEGE OF PHYSICAL EDUCATION, UDAIPUR (RAJASTHAN)
- BIRLA INSTITUTE OF TECHNOLOGY AND SCIENCE VIDYAVIHAR, PILANI- 333031. (RAJ)
- BOMBAY PHYSICAL CULTURE ASSOCIATION COLLEGE OF PHYSICAL EDUCATION, WADALA, MUMBAI. (MS)
- BVV SANGHA'S COLLEGE OF PHYSICAL EDUCAITON, BAGALKOT. DISTT: BIJAPUR. (KARNATAKA)
- CHANDERSHEKHAR AGASHEE COLLEGE OF PHYSICAL EDUCAITON, GULTEKADI, PUNE 411037 (MS)
- CHATRTRAPATI SHIVAJI COLLEGE OF PHYSICAL EDUCATION, NAGPUR.
- CHATTARAPATI SHIVAJI COLLEGE OF PHYSICAL EDUCATION, (BPED), KATOL-441302 (MS).

- CHAUDARY CHOTURAM COLLEGE OF PHYSICAL EDUCATION, MUZZAFFAR NAGAR, (U.P)
- CHAUDHRAY CHARAN SINGH UNIVERSITY, MEERUT-250005. (U.P)
- CHINTAMANI SHARIRIK SHIKSHAN MAHAVIDYALA, (BPED), WARDHA.
- COCHIN UNIVERSITY, KOCHI-682022, KERALA.
- COLLEGE OF PHYSICAL EDUCATION & MANAGEMENT STUDIES, BHOPAL (M.P)
- COLLEGE OF PHYSICAL EDUCATION, (BPE) AMALNER-425401. (NORTH MS)
- COLLEGE OF PHYSICAL EDUCATION, (BPE/BPED) JALGAON-425001. (NORTH MS)
- COLLEGE OF PHYSICAL EDUCATION, (BPED) NANDURBAR-425412 (NORTH MS)
- COLLEGE OF PHYSICAL EDUCATION, (BPED/MPED) CHOPDA. DISTT. JALGAON-425107. (NORTH MS)
- COLLEGE OF PHYSICAL EDUCATION, (MPED) BARSI. (MS)
- COLLEGE OF PHYSICAL EDUCATION, AHEMADNAGAR (MS)
- COLLEGE OF PHYSICAL EDUCATION, AHMEDABAD. (GUJARAT)
- COLLEGE OF PHYSICAL EDUCATION, GADCHIROLI
- COLLEGE OF PHYSICAL EDUCATION, KALINGA STADIUM, BHUBANESHWAR (ORISSA)
- COLLEGE OF PHYSICAL EDUCATION, KARANJA LAD
- COLLEGE OF PHYSICAL EDUCATION, MIRAJ (MS)
- COLLEGE OF PHYSICAL EDUCATION, NELLORE (A.P)

- COLLEGE OF PHYSICAL EDUCATION, SOLAPUR (MS)
- COLLEGE OF PHYSICAL EDUCATION, UMARKHED (MS)
- COLLEGE OF PHYSICAL EDUCATION, YAVATMAL (MS)
- COLLEGE OF SPORTS, HISSAR. HARYANA.
- DADASAHEB DIVAKER COLLEGE OF PHYSICAL EDUCATION, AKOLA. (MS)
- DADASAHEB RAMESHSING RAJPUT COLLEGE OF PHYSICAL EDUCATION, MALKAPUR (MS)
- DADASHEB RAMESH SINGH RAJPUT COLLEGE OF PHYSICAL EDUCATION, BULDHANA.
- DAYABHAI PATEL COLLEGE OF PHYSICAL EDUCATION, YAVATMAL (MS)
- DEGREE COLLEGE OF PHYSICAL EDUCATION, AMRAVATI (MS)
- DEGREE COLLEGE OF PHYSICAL EDUCATION, MEHAMADAVAD- 387 130, DISTT. KHEDA, GUJARAT
- DEOJIBHAU BUDHE MEMORIAL SHARIRIK SHIKSHAN MAHAVIDYALAYA, (BPED), GONDIA. (MS)
- DEPARTMENT OF PHYSICAL EDUCATION, ALAGAPPA UNIVERSITY COLLEGE OF PHYSICAL EDUCATION. ALAGAPA UNIVERSITY, KARAIKUDI–630003.
- DEPARTMENT OF PHYSICAL EDUCATION, ALIGARH MUSLIM UNIVERSITY, ALIGARH 202002, UTTAR PRADESH
- DEPARTMENT OF PHYSICAL EDUCATION, AMRAVATI UNIVERSITY, AMRAVATI-444602 (MS)
- DEPARTMENT OF PHYSICAL EDUCATION, BUNDELKHAND UNIVERSITY, JHANSI. (U.P)
- DEPARTMENT OF PHYSICAL EDUCATION, GUJARAT VIDYAPEETH, AHMEDABAD-380014. GUJARAT

- DEPARTMENT OF PHYSICAL EDUCATION, UNIVERSITY OF RAJASTHAN, UNIVERSITY, JAIPUR-302004. (RAJ)
- DEPTT. OF PHYSICAL EDUCATION RAJASTHAN AGRICULTURAL UNIVERSITY UDAIPUR-313001. (RAJ)
- DEPARTMENT OF PHYSICAL EDUCATION, KURUSHETRA UNIVERSITY, KURUSHETRA. HARYANA.
- DEPARTMENT OF PHYSICAL EDUCATION, MAHARISHI DAYANAND UNIVERSITY, ROHTAK. HARYANA.
- DEPARTMENT OF PHYSICAL EDUCATION, PT. R.S. SHUKLA UNIVERSITY, RAIPUR. (MP)
- DEPARTMENT OF PHYSICAL EDUCATION, RANI DURGAWATI UNIVERSITY, PACHPEDI, SARASWATI VIHAR, JABALPUR. (MS)
- DEPARTMENT OF STUDIES IN EDUCATION, MYSORE UNIVERSITY, MYSORE. (KARNATAKA)
- DEPTT. OF PHYSICAL EDUCATION AND SPORTS BABASAHEB BHIMRAO AMBEDKAR BIHAR UNIVERSITY, MUZZAFFARPUR (BIHAR) 842001.
- DEPTT. OF PHYSICAL EDUCATION AND SPORTS BANARAS HINDU UNIVERSITY, VARANASI-221005, UP.
- DEPTT. OF PHYSICAL EDUCATION AND SPORTS BANASTHLI VIDYAPITH, PO BANASTHALI VIDYAPITH-304022 (RAJ)
- DEPTT. OF PHYSICAL EDUCATION BANGALORE UNIVERSITY, BANGALORE - 560 056, KARNATAKA.
- DEPTT. OF PHYSICAL EDUCATION, ANDHRA UNIVERSITY, WALTAIR, VISAKHAPATNAM-530003, A.P
- DEPTT. OF PHYSICAL EDUCATION, GUJRAT UNIVERSITY, NAVRANGPURA, AHMEDABAD, GUJARAT.
- DEVI AHILYA VISHWAVIDYALAYA, INDORE - 452 001, MADYA PARDESH

- DEVIDUTT DALMIYA PHYSICAL EDUCATION TRAINING COLLEGE, JAIPUR. RAJASTHAN.
- DEWAJI BHAU BUDHE MEMORIAL COLLEGE OF PHY. EDU., BHANDARA. (MS)
- DHYANDIP SHIKSHAN PRASARAK MANDAL'S COLLEGE OF PHYSICAL EDUCATION, AMBAJOGAI-431517, DISTT. BEED. (MS)
- DHYANOPSAK COLLEGE OF PHYSCIAL EDUCATION, PARBHANI-431401. (MS)
- DHYANYOG SIKSHAN SANSTHA'S COLLEGE OF PHYSICAL EDUCATION, BHAKARDAN, DISTT. JALNA (MS)
- DILIP COLLEGE OF PHYSICAL EDUCATION, BARSI. (MS)
- DR. BABA SAHEB AMBEDKAR MARATHWADA UNIVERSITY, AURANGABAD -431 004, MAHARASHTRA
- DR. BABASAHEB NANDURKAR COLLEGE OF PHYSICAL EDUCATION, YAVATMAL.
- DR. BHIM RAO AMBEDKAR UNIVERSITY, AGRA-282 004. UTTAR PARDESH
- DR. HARI SINGH GAUR VISHWAVIDYALAYA, GAUR NAGAR, SAGAR-470 003 (MP)
- DR. R. M. LOHIA AVADH UNIVERSITY, FAIZABAD-224001. UTTAR PARDESH
- DR. SIVANTHI ADITANAR COLLEGE OF PHYSICAL EDUCATION, TRICHENDUR.
- DR. SUBHASH COLLEGE OF PHYSICAL EDUCATION, JUNAGARH. (RAJ)
- GANDHIGRAM RURAL INSTITUTE, GANDHIGRAM-624302. DISTT. DINDIGUL, T.N.

- GIRIJAN PHYSICAL EDUCATION COLLEGE, CHIKALDARA DISTRICT, AMRAVATI (MS)
- GOVERMENT COLLEGE OF PHYSICAL EDUCATION, HYDERABAD. (A.P)
- GOVERMENT COLLEGE OF PHYSICAL EDUCATION, KOZHIKODE.
- GOVERMENT WOMEN PHYSICAL EDUCATION COLLEGE, BILASPUR. (CHATISGARH)
- GOVINDRAO LUNGE SHARIRIK SIKSHAN MAHAVIDYALAYA, (BPED) MOWAD-441303. (MS)
- GOVINDRAO PAWAR COLLEGE OF PHYSICAL EDUCATION, KALAMB, DISTRICT YAVATMAL (MS)
- GOVT COLLEGE OF PHYSICAL EDUCATION, BHUBANESWAR. (ORISSA)
- GOVT COLLEGE OF PHYSICAL EDUCATION, RAMPUR. (U.P)
- GOVT COLLEGE OF PHYSICAL EDUCATION, SAMBALPUR. (M.P)
- GOVT. ARTS & SPORTS COLLEGE, JALANDHAR (PUNJAB)
- GOVT. COLLEGE OF PHYSICAL EDUCATION FOR WOMEN, DINHATA, COOCH BEHAR (W.B)
- GOVT. COLLEGE OF PHYSICAL EDUCATION, JODHPUR. (RAJ)
- GOVT. COLLEGE OF PHYSICAL EDUCATION, PATIALA, PUNJAB.
- GOVT. COLLEGE OF PHYSICAL EDUCATION, SRINAGAR (J & K)
- GOVT. PHYSICAL EDUCATION COLLEGE FOR WOMEN, HOOGLY-712103 (W.B)

- GOVT. WOMEN PHYSICAL EDUCATION COLLEGE, PENDRA ROAD, CHATTISGARH.
- GOVT. WOMENS PHYSICAL TRAINING COLLEGE, ALLAHABAD. U.P
- GRAMODAYA ASHRAM DEGREE COLLEGE, VEERSHINGPUR.
- GUJARAT AYURVED UNIVERSITY JAMNANAGAR-361008, GUJARAT.
- GULBARGA UNIVERSITY, "JNANA GANGA"GULBARGA-585106, KARNATAKA.
- GURU GHASIDAS UNIVERSITY, KONI BILASPUR-495005, CHHATTISGARH
- GURU NANAK DEV UNIVERSITY, AMRITSAR-143 005, PUNJAB
- GURUKUL KANGRI VISHWADIYALAYA, GURUKULAKANGRI HARDWAR-249404. UTTRANCHAL.
- H.V.P. MANDALS DEGREE COLLEGE OF PHYSICAL EDUCATION, AMRAVATI. (MS)
- HARISH MORE SHARIRIK SHIKSHAN MAHAVIDYALAYA, BHANDARA. (MS)
- HIMACHAL PRADESH UNIVERSITY, SUMMER HILLS, SHIMLA-171005, HIMACHAL PRADESH.
- HVKM COLLEGE OF PHYSICAL EDUCATION, YAVATMAL.
- INDIAN INSTITUTE OF TECHNOLOGY, CHENNAI-600036 T.N.
- INDIAN INSTITUTE OF TECHNOLOGY, KANPUR-208016 U.P.
- INDIRA GANDHI INSTITUTE OF PHYSICAL EDUCATION & SPORTS SCIENCES, VIKAS PURI, NEW DELHI-110018

- INDIRA GANDHI SHARIRIK SHIKSHAN MAHAVIDYALAYA, (BPED) NAGPUR
- INDIRA PRIYADARSHANI COLLEGE, (BPED/MPED) BHOPAL. (M.P)
- INDIRA SHIKSHAN PRASARAK MANDAL'S, COLLEGE OF PHYSICAL EDUCATION, LATUR.
- INDUTAI MEMORIAL B. P.ED COLLEGE, BULDANA
- INDUTAI MEMORIAL (BPED) COLLEGE OF PHYSICAL EDUCATION, NAGPUR
- ISHWAR DESHMUKH COLLEGE OF PHYSICAL EDUCATION, NAGPUR
- JADAVPUR UNIVERSITY, JADAVPUR, KOLKATTA-700 032 (W.B)
- JAGAT HARIHARBHAI SHARIRIK SHIKSHAN MAHAVIDYALAYA, (BPED), GOREGAON-441801. (GONDIA) (MS)
- JAI BAJRANG COLLEGE OF PHYSICAL EDUCATION, KUMBHARI DISTT., AKOLA. (MS)
- JAI HIND COLLEGE, BHOPAL.
- JAI KRANTI SHIKSHAN PRASARK MANDAL SWAMI DAYANAND COLLEGE OF PHYSICAL EDUCATION, (BPED) MIDC, LATUR (MS)
- JAI NARAIAN P. G. COLLEGE, LUCKNOW.
- JNANAJYOTHI COLLEGE OF PHYSICAL EDUCATION, BARALU - 573115, CHANNARAYAPATNA, DISTT. HASSAN (KARNATAKA)
- JANTA SHIKSHAN PRASARAK MANDAL'S B. P. ED COLLEGE OF PHYSICAL EDUCATION, PUSAD. DISTT. YAVATMAL (MS)
- JAWAHAR EDUCATION SOCIETY'S, KOLHAPUR

- JAWAHARLAL NEHRU UNIVERSITY, NEW DELHI-110067.
- JIWAJI UNIVERSITY, VIDYAVIHAR, GWALIOR-474011. MADHYA PRADESH
- JSP MANDAL'S COLLEGE OF PHYSICAL EDUCATION, KHULTABAD (MS)
- JUPITER SHARIRIK SHIKSHAN MAHAVIDYALAYA, NAGPUR,
- JYOTIBA COLLEGE OF PHYSICAL EDUCATION, (BPED) NAGPUR.
- K. D. PAWAR SHARIRIK SHIKSHAN MAHAVIDYALAYA, SAONER
- KAKATIYA UNIVERSITY, VIDYARANYAPURI, WARANGAD-506009. (A.P)
- KAMLA PRASAD SINGH DEGREE COLLEGE, RAMGARH
- KARMAVEER SIKSHAN SANSTHA COLLEGE OF PHYSICAL EDUCATION, JALANA (MS)
- KARNATAKA UNIVERSITY, PAVATE NAGAR, DHARWAD-580003, KARNATAKA
- KERALA AGRICULTURAL UNIVERSITY, VELLARIKKARA, THRISSUR-680654. KERALA.
- KISHAN MAHAVIDYALAYA, GAZIPUR.
- KRIDA MAHARSHI MEGHANATH NAGESHKAR SHARIRIK SIKSHAN SHASTRA MAHAVIDYALAYA, TARDEL
- KRISHI VIKAS PRATHAN'S COLLEGE OF PHYSICAL EDUCATION, BARAMATI DISTT. PUNE-413102 (MS)
- KURUKSHETRA UNIVERSITY, KURUKSHETRA-132119, HARYANA
- LAKSHMIBAI NATIONAL COLLEGE OF PHYSICAL EDUCATION, (LNCPE) THIRUVANANTHAPURAM, KERALA.

- LAKSHMIBAI NATIONAL INSTITUTE OF PHYSICAL EDUCATION, (LNIPE) SHAKTI NAGAR, GWALIOR-474002, MADHYAPARDESH.
- LATE BHS. TRUST'S COLLEGE OF PHYSICAL EDUCATION, MALEGOAN CAMP, DISTT. PUNE-423105 (MS)
- LATE DADARAO ADSAD SHARIRIK SHIKSHAN MAHAIDYALAYA, AMRAVATI.
- LATE MANORAMABAI DESHMUKH COLLEGE OF PHYSICAL EDUCATION, AMRAVATI. (MS)
- LATE NARAYAN SUNGH UIKEY SHARIRIK SHIKSHAN, CHANDRAPUR. (MS)
- LATE SH. VASANTRAO NAIK COLLEGE OF PHYSICAL EDUCATION, (B.PED) NAGPUR (MS)
- LOKHIT COLLEGE OF PHYSICAL EDUCATION, YAVATMAL. (MS)
- LUCKNOW CHRISTAIN COLLEGE OF PHYSICAL EDUCATION, LUCKNOW. (U.P)
- M. S. COLLEGE, MOTIHARI (BIHAR)
- M.D. COLLEGE OF RURAL SERVICE (AGRICULTURE), VYAYAM AND AROGYA SHIKSHAN VISHARAD (B.PED), RANDHEJA (AHMEDABAD) GUJARAT.
- M.D. COLLEGE OF SOCIAL SCIENCES (YOGA) AHMEDABAD.
- M.D. GRAM VIVASTHAPAN MAHAVIDYALAYA (B.PED), SADRA (GUJARAT).
- MADAN MOHAN MALVIYA COLLEGE (B.PED), KALAKANKAR. DISTT. PARAFAPGARH, U.P.
- MADHAVRAO WANKHEDE COLLEGE OF PHYSICAL EDUCATION, (M.PED), KAMPTEE, DISTT. NAGPUR (MS)
- MADURAI KAMRAJ UNIVERSITY, MADURAI (TN)

- MAGAS SAMAJ SEWA MANDALS COLLEGE OF PHYSICAL EDUCATION, SOLAPUR.
- MAHARANI LAXMIBAI VYAYAM MANDIR COLLEGE, KHANDER RAO GATE, JHANSI.
- MAHARISHI DAYANAND SARSWATI UNIVERSITY, AJMER- 305001 (RAJASTHAN).
- MAHARSHI VEDVYAS MAHAVIDYALAYA, M.P.
- MAHATMA EDUCATION SOCIETY'S VIDYADHIRAJA COLLEGE OF PHYSICAL EDUCATION & RESEARCH, NEW PANVEL, DISTT. RAIGAD, MAHARASHTRA.
- MAHATMA GANDHI KASHI VIDYAPITH, VARANASI, UTTAR PARDESH
- MAHATMA GANDHI UNIVERSITY, KOTTAYAM-686560, KERALA.
- MAHATMA JYOTIBA PHULE COLLEGE OF PHYSICAL EDUCATION, NAGPUR.
- MAHATMA JYOTIRAO FULEY SHARIRIK SHIKSHAN MAHAVIDYALAYA, (B.PED) UMERER-441203. (MS)
- MAJOR DHYANCHAND INSTITUTE OF PHYSICAL EDUCATION, BARKATULLAH VISHWAVIDYALAYA, BHOPAL-462026. (MP)
- MANGLORE UNIVERSITY, MANGALAGANGOTHRI-574193, KARNATAKA
- MANONMANIAM SUNDARNAR UNIVERSITY, TIRUNELVELI- 627008, TAMIL NADU.
- MARATHWADA SANSKRITIK MANDAL'S COLLEGE OF PHYSICAL EDUCATION, AURANGABAD.
- MATSYODRI SHIKSHAN SANSTHA'S COLLEGE OF PHY. EDU., JALNA .
- MODERN SHIKSHAN PRASARAK MANDAL'S COLLEGE OF PHYSICAL EDUCATION, AURANGABAD (MS)

- MOHANLAL SUKHADIA UNIVERSITY, UDAIPUR. (RAJASTHAN)
- MUNGSAJI MAHARAJ COLLEGE OF PHYSICAL EDUCATION, DARWHA-445202. (MS)
- MVAS. K. G NADGIR COLLEGE OF PHYSICAL EDUCATION, DHARWAD. (KARNATAKA)
- N. T. V. SAMITIS COLLEGE OF PHYSICAL EDUCATION, NANDURBAR. (DHULIA)
- NAGAJI MAHARAJ SHARIRIK SHIKSHAN MAHAVIDYALAYA, (BPED) NAGPUR. (MS)
- NAGARJUN COLLEGE OF PHYSICAL EDUCATION, NAGPUR.
- NAGARJUNA UNIVERSITY, NAGARJUNA NAGAR,-525510 DIST- GUNTUR. (A.P)
- NAGNATH COLLEGE OF PHYSICAL EDUCATION, PARBHANI.
- NAGPUR SHARIRIK SHIKSHAN MAHAVIDYALAYA, DHANTOLI, NAGPUR. (MS)
- NAGPUR UNIVERSITY, NAGPUR-444001, MAHARASTRA
- NANDANI NAGAR MAHAVIDYALAYA, NAWAB GANJ.
- NARAYAN PATIL (WASADE) COLLEGE OF PHYSICAL EDUCATION, (BPED) CHANDRAPUR (CRLY.) MS.
- NARAYAN SINGH UKEY SHARIRIK SIKSHAN MAHAVIDYALAYA, (BPED) CHIMUR-442903 (MS)
- NARAYANI DEVI VERMA MAHILA PHY T.T. COLLEGE, BHILWARA.
- NASHIKRAO TIRPUDE COLLEGE OF PHYSICAL EDUCATION, CIVIL LINES, SADAR, NAGPUR-440001. (MS)

- NAVGAN SHIKSHAN SANSTHA RAJURI'S COLLEGE OF PHYSICAL EDUCATION, BHIR (MS)
- NDMVP SAMAJ'S COLLEGE OF PHYSICAL EDUCATION, SHIVAJI NAGAR
- NETAJI SUBHAS NATIONAL INSTITUTE OF SPORTS, (NSNIS) PATIALA
- NETAJI SUBHASH CHANDER BOSE SHARIRIK SIKSHAN MAHAVIDYALAYA, AKLUJ (MS)
- NETAJI SUBHASHCHANDRA BOSE COLLEGE OF PHYSICAL EDU, AKLUJ.
- NIKHIL BANGA SIKSHAN MAHAVIDYALAYA, BISHNUPUR, BANKURA-722122. (WB)
- NOIDA COLLEGE OF PHYSICAL EDUCATION, NOIDA.
- NOOR KHAN SHIKSHAN SANSTHA, BHOPAL.
- NORTH GUJARAT UNIVERSITY, PATAN-384265, GUJARAT.
- NORTH MAHARASTRA UNIVERSITY, UMARINAGAR, JALGAON-425001, MAHARASHTRA
- OM SHANTI DHYAN MANDIR'S COLLEGE OF PHYSICAL EDUCATION, AMBAD, DIST. JALNA (MS)
- OSMANIA UNIVERSITY, HYDERABAD-500007, ANDRA PRADESH
- P. R. PATEL COLLEGE OF PHYSICAL EDUCATION, (BPED) PALASAR, (PATAN) NORTH GUJARAT.
- P.E.S COLLEGE OF PHYSICAL EDUCATION, AURANGABAD.
- P.G. COLLEGE, PATTI.
- P.M.COLLEGE OF PHYSICAL EDUCATION AND YOGA, TIGIRIA.

- PADAMSHRI AJIT WADEKAR SHARIRIK SHIKSHAN MAHAVIDYALAYA, (BPE/BPED) NAGPUR. (MS)
- PADMA RANI COLLEGE OF PHY.EDUCATION, AURANGABAD.
- PARVARA RURAL EDUCATION SOCIETY'S COLLEGE OF PHYSICAL EDUCATION, PRAVARNAGAR. TAL. SHRIRAMPUR, DISTT. AHMEDNAGAR. (MS)
- PAVANA SHIKSHAN PRASARAK MANDAL'S COLLEGE OF PHYSICAL EDUCATION, BHOSARI-411026, DISTT. PUNE (MS)
- PERIYAR UNIVERSITY, SALEM - 636011, TAMIL NADU
- PONDICHERRY UNIVERSITY, R. VENKATARAMAN NAGAR, KALAPET, PONDICHERRY-605014.
- POOJA SHARIRIK SHIKSHAN MAHAVIDYALAYA, (BPED) GONDIA (MS)
- POOJA SHARIRIK SHIKSHAN MAHAVIDYALAYA, BHANDARA.
- POST GRADUATE COLLEGE OF PHYSICAL EDUCATION, (NIZAM COLLEGE PREMISES) BASHEER BAGH, HYDERABAD- 500001 (A.P)
- POST GRADUATE TRAINING COLLEGE FOR PHYSICAL EDUCATION, BANIPUR, NORTH PARGANAS.
- PRABHURAJENDRA COLLEGE OF PHYSICAL EDUCATION, GADAG (KARNATAKA)
- PRAGATI SHIKSHAN SANSTHA JAWAHAR LAL NEHRU COLLEGE, BHOPAL.
- PRIYADARSHINI SHARIRIK SHIKSHAN MAHAVIDYALAYA, (BPED) NAGPUR
- PRIYADARSHNI SEVA SANSTHAN'S LATE DR. SHANKARRAO SATAV COLLEGE OF PHYSICAL EDUCATION, KALAMNURI. DISTT. HINGOLI (MS)

- PROF. RANGAS PHYSICAL EDUCATION INSTITUTE, DESHNOK.
- PUNJAB UNIVERSITY, SECTOR 14, CHANDIGARH-160014, PUNJAB.
- PUNJABI UNIVERSITY, PATIALA-147 002, PUNJAB.
- R. K. VAIDYA PRASARK MANDAL'S COLLEGE OF PHYSICAL EDUCATION, RANAWEDI, BAIL BAZAR, KALYAN, THANE
- R.S.K. MANDAL'S RAJRISHI SHAHU MAHARAJ COLLEGE OF PHYSICAL EDUCATION, AURANGABAD. (MS)
- RAJ. MAHILA T.T VIDYALAYA, UDAIPUR.
- RAJASTHAN VIDYAPEETH, UDAIPUR-313001 (RAJASTHAN)
- RAJIV GANDHI COLLEGE OF PHYSCIAL EDUCATION, AURANGABAD.
- RAJIV GANDHI COLLEGE OF PHYSICAL EDUCATION, BHOPAL. (MS)
- RAJURI COLLEGE OF PHYSICAL EDUCATION, BEED.
- RAMCHANDRA SANSKRITIK KRIDA MANDAL'S, JALANA.
- RAMESH DHAWAD COLLEGE OF PHYSICAL EDUCATION, (BPED) NAGPUR
- RANA PRATAP PHYSICAL TT SCHOOL, HITNA BHINDER.
- RANCHI UNIVERSITY, RANCHI- 834001.
- RANI LAXMIBAI SHARIRIK SHIKSHAN MAHAVIDYALAYA, (BPED) SAWARGAON-443208 (MS)
- RANIBAI AGNIHOTRI SHARIRIK SHIKSHAN MAHAVIDYALAYA, (BPED) WARDHA

- RANSAMRAT KRIDA MANDAL'S COLLEGE OF PHYSICAL EDUCATION, KALLAM, DIST. OSMANABAD
- RASHTRIYA SHARIRIK SHIKSHAN MAHAVIDYALAYA, CHANDRAPUR.
- RAYALASEEMA COLLEGE OF PHYSICAL EDUCATION, PRODDATUR, (CUDAPAH) (A.P)
- REGIONAL COLLEGE OF PHYSICAL EDUCATION, PANISAGAR.
- S.P.V.M.S. DAYABHAI PATEL COLLEGE OF PHYSICAL EDUCATION, YAVATMAL.
- S.S.S.P. MANDALS COLLEGE OF PHYSICAL EDUCATION, SOLAPUR.
- SADGURU EDUCATION SOCIETYS COLLEGE OF PHYSICAL EDUCATION, JALGAON.
- SHAHID BHAGAT SINGH PHYSICAL EDUCATION COLLEGE, AMRAVATI.
- SAIBABA SHARINIK SHIKSHANA MAHAVIDYALAYA, (BPED) GADCHIROLI (MS)
- SAKET COLLEGE OF PHYSICAL EDUCATION, (BPED) GONDIA. (MS)
- SAMBHALPUR UNIVERSITY, SAMBHALPUR
- SANATAN DHARAM PHYSICAL TT SANSTHAN, KEKRI.
- SANSKRUTI SANVARDHAN SHARIRIK SHIKSHAN MAHAVIDYALAYA, (BPE/BPED) NAGPUR
- SANT LAHANUJI MAHARAJ PHYSICAL EDUCATION COLLEGE, CHANDURPUR, AMRAVATI (MS)
- SARSWATI SIKSHAN SANSTHA'S SARASWATI COLLEGE OF PHYSICAL EDUCATION, NEW KAUTHA, NANDED-431603. (MS)

- SCHOOL OF STUDIES IN PHYSICAL EDUCATION AND SPORTS STUDIES, GWALIOR.
- SCHOOL OF STUDIES IN PHYSICAL EDUCATION, RAIPUR. (CHHATISGARH)
- SETH R.C.S ARTS AND COMMERCE COLLEGE, DURG. (CHHATISGARH)
- SHAHEED BHAGAT SING COLLEGE OF PHYSCIAL EDUCATION, AMRAVATI. (MS)
- SHAHEED KANSHI RAM COLLEGE OF PHYSICAL EDUCATION, (CPE/BPED) BHAGOO MAJRA. (PUNJAB)
- SHARIRIK SHIKSHAN MAHAVIDYALAYA, (BPED) AHERI (MS)
- SHARIRIK SHIKSHAN MAHAVIDYALAYA, (BPED) BHANDRA (MS)
- SHARIRIK SHIKSHAN MAHAVIDYALAYA, (BPED) CHANDRAPUR (MS)
- SHARIRIK SHIKSHAN MAHAVIDYALAYA, (BPED) GADCHANDUR (MS)
- SHARIRIK SHIKSHAN MAHAVIDYALAYA, (BPED) KAPARI (MS)
- SHARIRIK SHIKSHAN MAHAVIDYALAYA, (BPED) KORADI-441111. (MS)
- SHARIRIK SHIKSHAN MAHAVIDYALAYA, (BPED) MAUDA (MS)
- SHARIRIK SHIKSHAN MAHAVIDYALAYA, (BPED) SAKOLI-441802. (MS)
- SHARIRIK SHIKSHAN MAHAVIDYALAYA, (BPED) TUMSAR-441912. (MS)
- SHARIRIK SHIKSHAN MAHAVIDYALAYA, (BPED) WARORA (MS)

- SHARIRIK SHIKSHAN MAHAVIDYALAYA, KOLHAPUR
- SHARIRIK SHIKSHAN MAHAVIDYALAYA, KURUNDWAD (MS)
- SHARIRIK SHIKSHAN MAHAVIDYALAYA, MOHOL (MS)
- SHARIRIK SHIKSHAN MAHAVIDYALAYA, UCHAGAON (MS)
- SHARIRIK SIKSHA MAHAVIDYALAYA, SALGAR (MS)
- SHARIRIK SIKSHAN MAHAVIDYALAYA, (BPED) BALLARPUR-442701. (MS)
- SHARIRIK SIKSHAN MAHAVIDYALAYA, YAVATMAL
- SHETH C. N. VYAYAM VIDAY BHAWAN, COLLEGE OF PHYSICAL EDUCATION, AHMEDABAD. GUJARAT
- SHETKARI SHIKDHAN MANDALS COLLEGE OF PHYSICAL EDUCATION, BEED.
- SHETKARI SHIKSHAN PRASARAK MANDAL'S COLLEGE OF PHYSICAL EDUCATION, ASHTI. (MS)
- SHISHYA ACADEMY BPE COLLEGE, BARALU (KARNATAKA)
- SHIVAJI SHIKSHAN SANSTHA'S COLLEGE OF PHYSICAL EDUCATION, AMRAVATI.
- SHIVAJI UNIVERSITY, KOLHAPUR, MAHARASTRA.
- SHRAMJIVI SHIKSHAN PRASARAK MANDAL'S COLLEGE OF PHYSICAL EDUCATION, OMERGA-413606. (MS)
- SHREE NIKETAN COLLEGE OF PHYSICAL EDUCATION, (BPED) NAGPUR
- SHREE SWAMINARAYAN GURUKUL, KANSA, MEHSANA.
- SHRI AMBABAI TALEEM SANSTHAS COLLEGE OF PHYSICAL EDUCATION, MIRAJ.

- SHRI BABASAHEB GHARFALKAR COLLEGE OF PHY.EDUCATION, WARDHA.
- SHRI BAJRANG P.G. COLLEGE, SKIKENDERPUR.
- SHRI BALAJI COLLEGE OF PHYSICAL EDUCATION, AKOLA.
- SHRI BAPURAO DESHMUKH COLLEGE OF PHYSICAL EDUCATION, (BPED) WANDONGARI, NAGPUR
- SHRI C. P. SANATAK (DEGREE) VYAYAM MAHAVIDYALAYA, RAJPIPLA. DISTT. NARMADA. GUJARAT.
- SHRI CHATTRAPATI SHIVAJI COLLEGE OF PHYSICAL EDUCATION, SOLAPUR.
- SHRI CHHATRAPATI SHIKSHAN PRASARAK MANDAL'S COLLEGE OF PHYSICAL EDUCATION, OMERGA-413606 (MS)
- SHRI DWARAKA PHYSICAL TEACHER TRAINING COLLEGE, DESHNOK.
- SHRI GANDHI SAMARAK TRAINING COLLEGE OF PHYSICAL EDUCATION, SAMODHPUR.
- SHRI GANDHI T.T. COLLEGE, GULBABPURA.
- SHRI KRISHNA COLLEGE OF PHYSICAL EDUCATION, (BPED) WARDHA. (MS)
- SHRI KRUSHNARAO SATHONE SHARIRIK SHIKSHAN MAHAVIDYALAYA, (BPED) KAIRGAON (MS)
- SHRI MADHAVRAO WANKHEDE, COLLEGE OF PHYSICAL EDUCATION, NAGPUR.
- SHRI NAGARJUN SHARIRIK SIKSHAN MAHAVIDYALAYA, (BPED) RAMTEK-441106. (NAGPUR) MS.
- SHRI NARHEJI MAHAVIDYALAYA, NARHI

- SHRI NASIKRAO TIRPUDE COLLEGE OF PHYSICAL EDUCATION, CIVIL LINE, SADAR, NAGPUR-440001. (MS)
- SHRI RAMAKRISHNA VIDYALAYA MARUTI COLLEGE OF PHYSICAL EDUCATION, COIMBATORE.
- SHRI RAMRAO SARNAIK SHARIRIK SIKSHAN MAHAVIDYALAYA, WASHIM-444505. (MS)
- SHRI SACHDANAND COLLEGE OF PHYSICAL EDUCATION, NAGPUR.
- SHRI SEVADAS SHIKSHAN PRASARK MANDAL'S YESHWANT COLLEGE OF PHYSICAL EDUCATION, CIDCO, NEW NANDED-431603. (MS)
- SHRIKRISHNA SHARIRIK SHIKSHAN MAHAVIDYALAYA, WARDHA
- SHRIRAM PHYSICAL EDUCATION COLLEGE, DHAMANGAON. CRLY. (MS)
- SMT MADHURIBAI DESHMUKH SHARIRIK SHIKSHA MAHA-VIDYALAYA, WADI, NAGPUR-440023.
- SMT MENEKABA VYAYAM VIDYABHAWAN, ADALAJ (GANDHINAGAR) GUJARAT.
- SMT R. S. PATEL COLLEGE OF PHYSICAL EDUCATION, PATAN.
- SOUTH GUJARAT UNIVERSITY, SURAT.
- SRI BRAMARAMBHA MALIKARJUN COLLEGE OF PHYSICAL EDUCATION, KURNOOL (A.P)
- SRI JAI NARAIN DEGREE COLLEGE, LUCKNOW. (U.P)
- SRI KRISHNADEVARAYA UNIVERSITY, ANANTHAPUR - 515 003.
- SRI SARDA COLLEGE OF PHYSICAL EDUCATION FOR WOMEN, FAIRLANDS, SALEM-636016. (T.N)

- SRI VENKATAPATHAPPA COLLEGE OF PHYSICAL EDUCATION, CHICKBALLAPUR-562101, DISTT. KOLAR. (KARNATAKA)
- SRI VENKATESWARA UNIVERSITY, TIRUPATHI, 517 502.
- SRI. VIJAYNAGAR COLLEGE OF PHYSICAL EDUCATION, ANANTAPUR (A.P)
- SSR GOVERMENT COLLEGE OF PHYSICAL EDUCAITON, GOPANNAPELAM, (RLY. STATION – ELURU) WEST GODAVARI DISTT., A.P.
- STATE INSTITUTE OF PHYSICAL EDUCATION FOR WOMEN, KOLKATTA
- SUVIDHA EDUCATIONAL TRUST, MEHASANA.
- SWAMI RAMANAND TEERTH MARATHWADA UNIVERSITY, NANDED, MAHARASTRA.
- SWAMI SAMARTHA PHYSICAL EDUCATION COLLEGE, DHAMANGAON. C. RLY. (MS)
- SWAMI VIVEKANAND COLLEGE OF PHYSICAL EDUCATION, AHEMDABAD.
- TATYA TOPE STATE COLLEGE OF PHYSICAL EDUCATION, SHIVPURI. (M.P)
- TEA COLLEGE OF PHYSICAL EDUCATION, KOTTUR. (KARNATAKA)
- THE MAHARAJA SAYAJIRAO UNIVERSITY OF BARODA, VADODARA- 390002, GUJARAT.
- THE MULUND GYMKHANA'S COLLEGE OF PHYSICAL EDUCATION, MULUND, MUMBAI
- TILAK P.G. COLLEGE, AURAIYA.
- TIRUR PHYSICAL EDUCATION COLLEGE, HARUNGERI (KARNATAKA)

- UNIVERSITY COLLEGE OF PHYSICAL EDUCATION, MYSORE 570005
- UNIVERSITY OF BURDWAN, P.O. RAJBATI, DISTT. BURDWAN (W.B)
- UNIVERSITY OF CALCUTTA, KOLKATTA, WEST BENGAL - 700073
- UNIVERSITY OF CALICUT, CALICUT- 673635 - KERALA
- UNIVERSITY OF DELHI, DELHI - 110007
- UNIVERSITY OF HYDERABAD, HYDERABAD-500046. A.P
- UNIVERSITY OF JAMMU, JAMMU TAWI-180006. JK.
- UNIVERSITY OF KALYANI, KALYANI-741 235, WEST BENGAL
- UNIVERSITY OF KASHMIR, SRINAGAR-190 006, J&K
- UNIVERSITY OF KERELA, THIRUVANANTHAPURAM - 695034, KERELA
- UNIVERSITY OF LUCKNOW, LUCKNOW, UTTAR PARDESH
- UNIVERSITY OF MADRAS, TRIPLICANE, CHENNAI-600005. TAMIL NADU
- UNIVERSITY OF MUMBAI, MUMBAI 400 032, MAHARASTRA
- UNIVERSITY OF MYSORE, MYSORE, KARNATAKA
- UNIVERSITY OF NORTH BENGAL, DARJEELING, WEST BENGAL
- UNIVERSITY OF PUNE, GANESHKHIND, PUNE-411007, MAHARASHTRA
- UTKAL UNIVERSITY, BHUBANESHWAR, ORISSA
- V. N. S. COLLEGE OF PHYSICAL EDUCATION AND MANAGEMENT STUDIES, BHOPAL.

- V. S. S. PHYSICAL EDUCATION COLLEGE, KULUNDI (ORISSA)
- VIDARBHA SHARIRIK SHIKSHAN MAHAVIDYALAYA, CHANDRAPUR.
- VIDARBHA YUVAK VIKAS SANSTHA'S COLLEGE OF PHYSICAL EDUCATION, BULDANA
- VISHVA BHARTI, DIST. BIRBHUM, WEST BENGAL-731 235.
- VSM'S COLLEGE OF PHYSICAL EDUCATION, SATARA. (MS)
- WAINGANGA COLLEGE OF PHYSICAL EDUCATION, BHANDARA.
- YASHWANT RAO CHAVAN COLLEGE OF PHYSCIAL EDUCATION, WASHIM. (MS)
- YASHWANTRAO CHAVAN PHYSICAL EDUCATION COLLEGE, MANGRULPIR (MS)
- YESHODIP SHIKSHAN SANSTHA'S NAGNATH COLLEGE OF PHYSICAL EDUCATION, (BPED) JAWALA BAZAR, DIST. HINGOLI.
- YESHWANT COLLEGE OF PHYSICAL EDUCATION, NEW NANDED.
- YMCA COLLEGE OF PHYSICAL EDUCATION, CHENNAI.
- YUVA VYAVASAIK SHIKSHAN SANSTHAN, GUNA.
- YUVASHAKTI B.P.ED. COLLEGE, AMRAVATI (MS)
- YUVASHAKTI SHARIRIK SHIKSHAN MAHAVIDYALAYA, AMRAVATI.
- ZION COLLEGE OF PHYSICAL EDUCATION, CUDAPPAH. (A.P)

Directorates of Sports in Indian Universities

Sports Officer,
Agra University,
Agra - 282004 (U.P)

Dean, Physical Education,
Alagappa University,
Alagappapuram,
Karaikudi - 623003 (T.N)

Secretary Games Committee,
Aligarh Muslim University,
Aligarh - 202002 (U.P)

Director of Sports,
Amravati University,
Tapown Road Camp,
Amravati - 444602 (Maharashtra)

Director, Physical Education,
Andhra University,
Visakhapatnam - 530003 (A.P)

Director of Sports,
Anna University,
Sardar Patel Road,
Guindy, Chennai- 600025 (T.N)

Director Physical Education,
Annamalai University.
P.O. Annamalaingar - 608002
South Arcot Distt. Cuddalore (T.N)

Director of Sports,
Avinashilingam Institute for Home Science and Higher Education for Women,
Coimbatore - 641043 (T.N.)

Director Physical Education,
Awadhesh Pratap Singh University,
Rewa - 486003 (MP)

Director (Sports),
Babasaheb Bhimrao Ambedkar Bihar University,
Muzaffarpur - 842001 (Bihar)

Vice-President Sports Board,
Banaras Hindu University,
Varanasi - 221005 (U.P.)

Director of Sports,
Banasthali Vidyapith,
P.O. Banasthali Vidyapith -304022 (Raj.)

Director of Sports,
Bangalore University,
Jnana Bharathi,
Bangalore - 560056 (Karnataka)

Director Physical Education,
Barkatullah Vishwavidyalaya,
Hoshangabad Road,
Bhopal - 462026 (M.P)

Director Physical Education,
The Maharaja Sayajirao University of Baroda,
Opp. Drug Laboratory, Shastri Bridge Road, Fatehgani,
Vadodara -390002

Secretary Sports Council,
Berhampur University,
Bhanja Bihar, Berhampur, - 760007
Distt. Ganjam (Orissa)

Director Sports,
Bharathiar University,
Maruthamalai Road,
Coimbatore 641046. (T.N.)

Director Sports,
Bharathidasan University,
Palkalaiperur,
Tiruchirapalli 620024 (T.N.)

Director (Sports)
Bharti Vidyapeeth,
Bharti Vidyapeeth Bhavan,
Lal Bahadur Shastri Marg,
Pune - 411030 (Maharastra)

Director of Sports,
Bhavnagar University,
Gaurishanker Lake Road,
Bhavnagar 364002 (Gujarat)

Director Sports,
Birla Institute of Technology,
Mesra - 835215
Distt. Ranchi (Jharkhand)

Director of Physical Education,
Birla Institute of Technology and Science,
Vidya Vihar, Pilani - 333031 (Raj,)

Sports Officer,
Bundelkhand University,
Jhansi - 284128 (U.P)

Director Students Welfare / Sports,
University of Mumbai, M.G. Road,
Fort, Mumbai - 400032 (Maharashtra)

Director Physical Education,
University of Calicut,
Calicut University P.O. Malappuram Distt.
Calicut - 673635 (Kerala)

Chairman of Sport Council,
Chaudhary Charan Singh University,
Meerut - 250005 (U.P)

Dean (Sports)
C.C.S Haryana Agricultural University,
Hisar - 125004 (Haryana)

Asstt. Director Physical Education,
Cochin University of Science and Technology,
Cochin University P.O., Kochi - 682022 (Kerala)

Sports Officer,
Dayalbag Educational Institute, Dayalbagh,
Agra - 282005 (U.P)

Director Sports ,
Deccan College Post Graduate and Research Institute,
Yervada, Pune 411006 (Maharashtra)

Director Physical Education and Sports,
University of Delhi,
Delhi - 110007

Director Physical Education (Sports),
Devi Ahilya Vishwavidyalaya,
Nalanda Parisar, 169 Ravindra Nath Tagor Marg,
Indore - 452001 (M.P)

Dean, Physical Education,
Dr. Babasaheb Ambedkar Marathwada University,
Aurangabad - 431004 (Maharashtra)

Director,
Dr. bhim Rao Ambedkar University,
Senate House, Paliwal Park,
Agra - 284004 (U.P)

Director of Sports,
Doctor Hari Singh Gour Vishwavidaylaya,
Gour Nagar, Sagar - 470003 (M.P.)

President Sports Council,
Dr. Ram Manohar Lohia University,
Faizabad - 224001 (U.P)

Director of Physical Education,
Gandhigram Rural Institute,
Gandhigram - 624302
Distt. Dindigul (T.N.)

Director of Sports,
University of Gorakhpur,
Gorakhpur - 273009 (UP)

Director (Sports),
Govind Ballabh Pant University of Agriculture and Technology,
Pantnagar - 263145
Udam Singh Nagar (Uttranchal Pradesh)

Director of Physical Education,
Gujarat Ayurved University, Admninistrative Bhavan
Irwin Hospital Road,
Jamnagar 361008 (Gujarat)

Director Physical Education,
Gujarat University,
Navrangpura,
Ahmedabad - 380009 (Gujarat)

Director Sports,
Gujarat Vidyapith,
P.O. Navjivan, Ashram Road
Ahmedabad - 380014 (Gujarat)

Director of Sports,
Gulbarga University,
Jnana Ganga,
Gulbarga - 585106 (Karnataka)

Director of Sports,
Guru Ghasidas University,
P.O. Koni,
Bilaspur - 495009 (Chhattisgarh)

Director Physical Education and Sports
Gurukul Kangri Vishwavidyalaya
P.O Gurukul Kangri
Hardwar (Uttranchal Pradesh)

Director of Sports and Physical Education,
Guru Nank Dev University,
Amritsar - 143005 (Punjab)

Director of Sports,
Hemwati Nandan Bahuguna Garhwal University,
Srinagar - 246174
Garhwal (Uttranchal Pradesh)

Director of Sports,
Himachal Pradesh University,
Summer Hills, Shimla - 171005 (Himachal Pradesh)

Director of Sports,
University of Hyderabad,
P.O. Central University,
Hyderabad 500046 (Andhra Pradesh)

Chairman, Sport Activities
Indian Institute of Technology,
P.O. IIT Powai,
Mumbai - 400076 (Maharashtra)

President Sports Board,
Indian Institue of Technology,
Hauz Khas, New Delhi - 110016

Physical Education Officer,
Indian Institute of Technology,
IIT Post Office, Kalyanpur
Kanpur - 208016 (U.P)

Adviser, Sports Activities,
Indian Institute of Technology,
IIT P.O. Chennai - 600036

Sports Officer,
Indian School of Mines,
Dhanbad - 826004 (Jharkhand)

Director of Sports,
Indira Kala Sangit Vishwavidyalaya,
Khairagarh - 491881
Distt. Rajnandgaon (MP)

Sports Incharge,
International Institute for Population Sciences,
Govandi Station Road, Deonar,
Mumbai - 400088 (Maharashtra)

President, Sports Board,
Jai Narain Vyas University
Jodhpur - 342001 (Rajasthan)

Secretary, Sports Council,
Jai Prakash Vishwavidyalaya,
Dak Bungalow Road,
Chapra - 841301 (Bihar)

Director of Sports,
Jamia Millia Islamia,
Mohammad Ali Jauhar Marg,
Jamia Nagar,
New Delhi 110025

Director of Physical Education
Jammu University,
Jammu. (J&K)

Director of Sports,
Jawaharlal Nehru University,
New Mehrauli Road,
New Delhi -110067

Director Physical Education,
Jiwaji University,
Vidya Vihar,
Gwalior - 474011 (MP)

Director of Sports,
Kakatiya University,
Vidyaranyapuri,
Warangal - 506009 (Andhra Pradesh)

Director of Sports,
University of Kalyani,
P.O. Kalyani. - 741235
Distt. Nadia (West Bengal)

Sports Incharge,
K. S. Darbhanga Sanskrit University,
Kameshwarnagar, Darbhanga - 846008 (Bihar)

Director of Sports,
Karnatak University,
Pavate Nagar,
Dharwad - 580003 (Karnataka)

Chairman, Sports Council
Mahatama Ghandhi Kashi Vidyapīth,
Varanasi - 221002 (UP)

Director of Physical Education,
University of Kashmir,
University Campus, Hazratbal,
Srinagar - 190006 (J&K)

Director of Physical Education,
University of Kerala, University P.O.
Thiruvanathapuram - 695034 (Kerala)

Sports Officer,
Konkan Krishi Vidyapeeth,
Dapoli, Distt. - 415712
Ratnagiri (Maharashtra)

Director of Sports,
Kurukshetra University,
Kurukshetra - 136119 (Haryana)

Director of Sports,
Kuvempu University,
Jnana Sahyadri, B.R. Project,
Shimoga Distt. 577115 (Karnataka)

Director, Physical Education,
University of Madras,
Centenary Buildings Chepauk, Triplicane P.O.
Chennai - 600005 (T. N)

Director of Sports,
Madurai - Kamaraj University,
Palkalai Agar, Madurai - 625021 (T. N)

Director, Physical Education,
Maharshi Dayanad Saraswati University,
Ajmer - 305001 (Rajasthan)

Director of Sports,
Mahatma Gandhi University,
Priyadarshini Hills P.O.
Kottayam - 686560 (Kerala)

Sports Incharge,
Makhanlal Chaturvedi National University,
E-8, Area Colony, P.B. No. RSN/60
Bhopal - 462016 (M.P)

Director of Sports,
Mangalore University,
University Campus
Mangalagangothri - 574199 (Karnataka)

Director of Sports,
Manipur University,
Canchipur, Imphal - 795003 (Manipur)

Assist. Director of Physical Education,
Manonmaniam Sundaranar University,
University Campus,
Abishekapatti, Tirunelveli - 627008 (T.N)

Director of Sports,
Marathwada Krishi Vidyapeeth,
Krishi Nagar,
Parbhani - 431402 (Maharashtra)

Secretary Sports Board,
Mohanlal Sukhadia University,
Pratap nagar, Udaipur - 313001 (Raj.)

Director of Sports,
University of Mysore,
Crawford Hall,
Mysore - 570005 (Karnataka)

Director Sports,
Nagaland University,
Lumami (HQ) Kohima - 797001 (Nagaland)

Directors of Physical Education,
Nagarjuna University,
Nagarjuna Nagar - 525510
Distt. Guntur (A.P)

Director of Sports,
Nagpur University,
Ravindra Nath Tagore Marg,
Nagpur - 440001 (Maharashtra)

Director of Sports,
North-Eastern Hill University,
NEHU, Permanent Campus,
Mawkynrow Umshing,
Shillong - 793022, (Meghalaya)

Director of Sports,
North Gujarat University,
PB No. 21, Rajmahel Road,
Patan - 384265 (Gujarat)

Director of Sports,
North Maharashtra University,
P.O. No. 80, NH No.6,
ITI Hostel, Jalgaon - 425001 (Maharashtra)

Director of Sports,
Osmania University,
Administrative Building,
Hyderabad - 500007 (A.P)

Director of Sports,
Punjab University,
Sector-14, Chandigarh - 160014

Secretary Sports,
Patna University,
Patna - 800005 (Bihar)

Director of Physical Education,
Periyar University
Govt College of Engineerign Campus,
Salem - 636011 (T.N)

Director of Physical Education,
Pondicherry University
R. Venkataraman Nagar,
Kalapet, Pondicherry - 605014

Director of Sports,
University of Pune,
Ganeshkhind, Pune - 411007 (Maharashtra)

Director of Sports,
Punjabi University,
Patiala - 147002 (Punjab)

Sports Officer,
Rabindra Bharati University,
Emerald Bower Campus,
56/A, BT Road, Kolkatta - 700050 (West Bengal)

Director of Sports,
Rajashtan Vidyapeeth,
Udaipur - 313001 (Rajasthan)

Director Physical Education,
Ranchi University,
Ranchi - 834001 (Jharkhand)

Director of Sports,
Rani Durgavati Vishwavidyalaya,
Saraswati Vihar, Pachpedi,
Jabalpur - 482001 (M.P)

Sports Secretary,
Rohilkhand University,
University Campus,
Bareilly - 243001 (U.P.)

Director of Sports,
University of Roorkee,
Roorkee - 247667 (U.P)

Director of Sport,
Sampurnanand Sanskrit Vishvavidyalaya,
Varanasi - 221002 (U.P)

Director of Sports,
Sardar Patel University,
Vallabh Vidyanagar - 388120 (Gujarat)

Director of Sports,
Saurashtra University,
University Road,
Rajkot - 360005 (Gujarat)

Director of Sports,
School of Planning and Architecture,
4, Block-B, Indraprastha Estate,
New Delhi -110002

Director of Sports,
Shreemati Nathibai Damodar Thackersey Women's University,
1, Nathibai Thackersey Road,
Mumbai - 400020 (Maharashtra)

Incharge Sports,
Siddu Kanhu University,
Santal Partganas, Dumka - 814101 (Bihar)

Director of Physical Education,
Sri Krishnadevaraya University,
Sri Venkateswarapuram,
Anantapur - 515003 (A.P)

Director of Sports,
Sri Padmavati Mahila Visvavidyalayam,
Tirupati - 517502, Chittoor Distt. (A.P)

Director of Physical Education,
Sri Venkateswara University,
Tirupati - 517502 Chittoor Distt. (A.P)

Dean, Physical Education,
Swami Ramanand Teerath Marathwada University,
Dnyanteerth, Gautami Nagar,
Vishnupuri, Nanded - 431606 (Maharastra)

Director Physical Education,
Tamil Nadu Agriculture University,
Coimbatore - 641003 (T. N)

Director of Sports,
Thapar Institute of Engineering and Technology,
P.O. Patiala -147001 (Punjab)

Director of Sports,
University of Agricultural Sciences,
Gandhi Krishi Vignana,
Kendra Campus,
Bangalore - 560065 (Karnataka)

Director of Sports,
Vikaram University,
Kothi Road,
Ujjain - 456010 (M.P)

Director of Physical Education,
Visva-Bharati, P.O. Santiniketan,
Distt. Birhum - 731235 (West Bengal)

List of Recognised National Sports Federations Approved by Dept. of Youth Affairs & Sports and Affiliated to Indian Olympic Assocaition

All India Carrom Federation,
South Plaza, Indra Gandhi Indoor Stadium,
I. P. Estates, New Delhi - 110 002

All India Chess Federation,
III/37,NonaManzil,
Post Nallalam, Calicut. (Kerala)

All India Football Federation,
Netaji Indoor Stadium,
Eden Garden, Calcutta. West Bengal.

All India Karate Do Federation,
ITTS House, 6th floor,
28 K Dubhash Marg,
Mumbai - 400023 Maharastra

All India Lawn Tennis Association,
B-3/7, Asaf Ali Road,
New Delhi.

All India Sports Council of Deaf,
8, Northend Complex,
Shri Ramakrishna Ashram Marg, New Delhi.

All India Tennis Association
R K Khanna Tennis Stadium,
Africa Avenue, New Delhi.

Aero Club of India,
Safdarjung Airport, Aurobindo Marg,
New Delhi.

Amateur Athletic Federation of India,
Room No. 1148-A, Gate No. 28,
Jawaharlal Nehru Stadium, New Delhi.

Amateur Baseball Federation of India,
Pocket E-19/12-13, Rohini
Delhi - 110 085.

Amateur Kabaddi Federation of India,
2, AAKANKSHA, Ajmer Raod,
Jaipur - 302019

Archery Association of India,
6, Bishamber Das Marg,
New Delhi

Atya Patya Federation of India,
Nagpur Sharirik Shikshan Mahavidyalaya,
Dr. Moonga Marg,
Dhantoli, Nagpur.(Maharashtra)

Badminton Association of India,
Jackson Hotel, Civil Line,
Jabalpur (MP)

Ball Badminton Federation of India,
A- 15 Chandra Mahal Colony,
Chini Ki Buraj, Chboti Chooper, Jaipur.

Basketball Federation of India,
Trishill Flat 1A,
35 Rowland Road, Calcutta.

Billiards & Snooker Federation of India,
C/o The Bengal Bonded Warehouse Association,
25, Netaji Subhas Road, Kolkatta. (W.B)

Board of Control for Cricket in India,
Cricket Association of Bengal,
Dr. B.C. Roy Club House,
Eden Gardens, Kolkatta. (W.B)

Bowling Federation of India
Shanti Farm Village Chandanhula
Delhi

Bridge Federation of India,
1-2-307, Dornalguda
Hyderabad.

Cycle Polo Federation of India,
20, Aurangzeb Road,
New Delhi

Cycling Federation of India,
Yamuna Velodrome,
Indira Gandhi Stadium Complex, New Delhi.

Equestrian Federation of India,
764-B, Gate 29, Jawaharlal Nehru Stadium,
New Delhi.

Fensing Assocaition of India
1152, Ist Floor, Gate No 28
J. N. Stadium, Lodhi Road,
New Delhi

Federation of Motor Sports Club of India,
McDowell House, 2nd Line Beach, P.B. No. 1256,
Chennai . (T.N)

Gymnastics Federation of India,
160 A, Gate No 28 J. N. Stadium
New Delhi

Handball Federation of India
1526, Sector C Pocket 1
Vasant Kunj, New Delhi

Indian Amateur Boxing Federation,
158-A, Gate No. 28,
Jawaharlal Nehru Stadium, New Delhi.

Indian Body Building Federation,
46 Ridge Road, Rekha Building,
Malabar Hill, Mumbai

Indian Golf Union,
Tata Centre, 3rd Floor, 43, Chowringhee Road, Kolkatta (W.B)

Indian Hockey Federation,
Room No. 186, National Stadium,
New Delhi.

Indian Kayaking & Canoeing Association,
606, Akash Deep, 6th Floor, Barakhamba Road,
Connaught Place, New Delhi.

Indian Mountaineering Foundation,
Benito Juarez Road,
Anand Niketan, New Delhi.

Indian Powerlifting Federation,
98,New Ranikudar,
Jamshedpur. (Bihar)

Indian Polo Association,
C/o President's Body Guard, Gate No. 24, Rashtrapati Bhavan, New Delhi.

Indian Triathlon Federations
Dhuu Building, 3 rd Floor,
Northwing, 827 Annu Salni, Chennai.

Indian Style Wrestling Federation of India,
NIS Wrestling Coach, House No. 1335, Sector 17,
Defence Colony, Gurgaon (Haryana).

Indian Weightlifting Federation,
Gate No 5, J. N. Stadium
New Delhi

Indian Women's Hockey Federation,
Shivaji Stadium,
New Delhi.

Judo Federation of India,
Room No 1134, Gate no 27,
J. N. Stadium,
New Delhi

Kho Kho Federation of India,
65/2 Hindustan Park,
Calcutta

Mallakhamb Federation (Regd) India
B-14 Shanti Mogal Lane
Mahim, Mumbai

Motor Sports Club of India
Krishna Tower - 1 6 th floor
Aptt. 25 9-13 Sardar Patel Road,
Chennai

National Rifle Association,
Gate No 26, J. N. Stadium
New Delhi

Netball Association of India
1108, Sector C- 1,
Vasant Kunj, New Delhi

Roller Skating Federation of India,
14/2, Civil Road,
Kolkatta. (W.B)

Rowing Federation of India,
Gate No 28 J. N. Stadium
New Delhi

Services Sports Control Board,
Armed Forces Headquaters
G- Block DHQ
New Delhi

Shooting Ball Federation of India,
S-28, Green Park Extension,
New Delhi.

Softball Association of India,
Dr. Shivajee Sarode,
214 Navi Pietts, Station Road,
Jalgaon.

Squash Racket Federation of India,
C/o. The Calcutta Racket Club, Near St. Paul's Cathedral, Chowringhee, Kolkatta. (W.B)

Swimming Federation of India,
Gift land 3, Aminabad.
Lucknow

Table Tennis Federation of India,
R. No. 1144-A, 1st Floor, Gate No. 28,
Jawaharlal Nehru Stadium, New Delhi.

Taekwondo Federation of India,
RZ - 85 Bhawani Kunj,
Pocket D- 11 Vasant Kunj
New Delhi

Tennikoit Federation of India,
Room No. 159, Ground Floor, 3rd Cross,
2nd Main, Dattatreya Extension,
Bangalore. (Karnataka)

Throwball Federation of India,
29, Raja Ram Mohan Roy Road,
Bangalore. (Karnataka)

Volleyball Federation of India,
160 B Gate No 28, J. N. Stadium
New Delhi

Winter Games Federation of India
D- 502, Som Vihar, Sangam Road,
R. K. Puram, New Delhi - 110 002

Women's Cricket Association of India,
174, Ramesh Dutta Street,
Kolkatta. (W.B)

Women's Football Federation of India,
Behind Head Post Office, Main Bazaar,
Gorakhpur, Uttar Pradesh.

Wrestling Federation of India,
South Plaza, Under Pylon 3, I.G. Stadium,
New Delhi.

Yachting Association of India,
Room No. 33, Directorate of Naval Training,
'C' Wing, Sena Bhavan,
New Delhi.

Yoga Federation of India
247/1 Sector 14
Panchkula - 134109